Cosmic Impact

Cosmic Impact

John Keith Davies

Fourth Estate · London

First published in Great Britain in 1986 by
Fourth Estate Ltd
113 Westbourne Grove
London W2 4UP
Telephone: 01-727 8993, 243 1382

Copyright © John K. Davies

British Library Cataloguing in Publication Data

Davies, John K.
  Cosmic impact.
  1. Planets, Minor
  I. Title
  523.4'4   QB651

ISBN 0-947795-20-0

Phototypeset in 11/12 Bembo by
AKM Associates (UK) Ltd, Ajmal House, Hayes Road, Southall, London
Printed and bound by
Billings and Sons Ltd, Worcester

To Mum and Dad

Contents

Acknowledgements

I would like to take this opportunity to thank everyone who made *Cosmic Impact* possible: Doug Whittet and Ian Robson at Lancashire Polytechnic, who gave me my first chance to do professional astronomy; Jack Meadows of Leicester University, who introduced me to the study of Earth-crossing objects; and especially Simon Green, Brian Stewart, Peter Clegg, Eric Dunford and the rest of the American, Dutch and British IRAS team who made it possible for me to discover some.

I have received considerable help from interested scientists around the world, too numerous to mention individually, who sent me details of their work on asteroids, impacts and evolution and I am also grateful to A. Hallam, Lapworth Professor of Geology at Birmingham University, for his help in understanding the debate concerning the extinction of the dinosaurs. Responsibilities for any misrepresentation of their work, of course, remain firmly at my door.

Finally I should thank Michael Mason and William Radzinowicz of Fourth Estate for guiding me along during the preparation of my first book, and to my wife Maggie for putting up with the many hours writing it has taken me from her side.

Illustration Credits

I would like to thank the following individuals and organizations who were kind enough to provide me with photographs for use in *Cosmic Impact*.

Don Gault, Murphys Centre for Planetology, USA.
Richard Grieve and Blyth Robertson, Dept of Energy, Mines and Resources, Ottawa, Canada.
Ian Halliday, Herzberg Institute of Astrophysics, Ottawa.
Colin Jones, Australia House, London.
Dr Charles Kowal, California Institute of Technology.
Leicestershire Museums.
M.P.I. für Aeronomie, Lindau.
J. C. Muirhead, Defence Research Establishment, Suffield, Canada.
NASA Jet Propulsion Laboratory, Pasadena, California.
Novosti Press Agency, London.
Royal Greenwich Observatory, London.
Royal Observatory, Edinburgh.
Melita Webster, Australian News and Information Service, London.
US Geological Survey.

The figure on page 108 is based on the work of Dr D.J. Roddy, published in *Impact and Explosion Cratering*, Eds Roddy, Perrin and Merill (Pergamon Press, New York, 1977).

Some Notes on Units

Following the widely accepted conventions for scientific writing, the metric system has been used throughout *Cosmic Impact*. For the convenience of readers unfamiliar with these units some conversion factors are given below.

1 metre = 39.37 inches
1 kilometre = 1000 metres = 0.621 miles
1 kilogram = 2.2 lb
1 tonne = 1000 kilograms = 0.917 imperial ton = 1.1 short tons

1 megaton = the explosive power of 1 million tons of TNT
1 megaton = 4.2×10^{22} ergs = 4.2×10^{15} joules

1

Stones from the Sky

On an overcast Christmas Eve, 1965, Howard Miles was in the kitchen of his house near Coventry when he saw what he later described as a blinding flash. Thinking it was lightning, he began to count seconds, waiting for the accompanying thunder – but when the noise arrived it was not thunder but a single loud bang. Looking outside he saw, through a hole in the clouds, a trail of smoke across the sky which he imagined to be the result of a firework let off by a premature Christmas reveller. For the moment, he thought nothing more about it.

Howard Miles was not alone; throughout the Coventry area about 50 people glimpsed a light, described by some as orange-red in colour, moving rapidly across the sky. Many others saw nothing but heard a prolonged rumble, or a bang, or both. Thirty kilometres to the north-east there were neither flashes nor bangs, just a swishing noise followed by a series of dull thuds. The time was 4.12 p.m. and in Barwell, Leicestershire, the sky was falling.

Few people in Barwell actually saw anything strike the ground although one villager, Mr Crow, was severely shaken when a piece of stone weighing almost three kilograms buried itself in the earth a few metres from where he was standing. Thinking he was under some sort of rocket attack, Mr Crow took shelter behind a wall. Close by, a one-and-a-half-kilogram stone penetrated 30 centimetres into the soil of a neighbour's garden. Further down the street a slightly smaller object struck the tarmac road surface and disintegrated, smashing two windows in a nearby house and leaving a fragment hidden in a bowl of artificial flowers. Another object, weighing about three kilograms, struck a parked car, causing surprisingly little damage. The car owner, suspecting a schoolboy prank, threw the stone away.

Across the village, a few hundred metres away, another falling stone made a hole 25 centimetres in diameter and 15 centimetres deep in the driveway of a private house, and at a local knitwear factory a 400–gram object crashed through the asbestos roof and continued down through the floorboards. A larger piece was found 60 metres away in the factory yard. The factory was closed for Christmas, so no one was hurt.

The villagers soon realized that they were not the victims of a rocket attack, or of vandalism. Barwell had been struck by a shower of meteorites, fragments of an object which had collided with the Earth and broken up during its flight through the atmosphere, showering the village with debris.

News of the fall soon reached Howard Miles, a member of the British Astronomical Association, and he realized that the flash he had seen from his kitchen window was the fireball caused by the object's entry and that it was the bang of a sonic boom, not a firework, which he had heard on Christmas Eve. Aware of the importance of collecting as many fragments as possible, he travelled to Barwell and there, with the help of the village constable, searched the fields and found several recently fallen meteorites. Other specimens were later recovered from local schoolchildren who, with commendable commercial, if not scientific motives, had located several small fragments and were negotiating their disposal. Other pieces came to light over the next few months, the largest, which weighed nearly eight kilograms, being found after the British Museum had offered the then considerable sum of ten shillings per ounce (28 gm) for pieces weighing more than two pounds (0.9 kg). The finder of this fragment, which was located at the bottom of a 60–centimetre-deep vertical hole, was awarded £140. In total over 40 kilograms of material were collected.

Analysis of eyewitness reports from various places in the Midlands showed that not one, but three separate fireballs had been seen. From this scientists were able to deduce that during its flight through the atmosphere the object had first split into two pieces, one of which subsequently split again. It was one of these second-generation fragments which disintegrated and scattered meteorites across Barwell. No pieces of the other two fireballs have ever been found and they may have burned up completely. Despite the failure to find fragments of the other two objects, the material collected at Barwell represents the largest known meteorite fall in the United Kingdom.

In many ways the villagers of Barwell were lucky. Not only did the majority of the meteorites which fell that afternoon land short of the village, but the total mass of material involved was quite small. A considerably more devastating fall had occurred about 20 years earlier on the western spurs of the Sikhote-Alin mountain region of the Soviet Union, when a 70–tonne object disintegrated during atmospheric entry and scattered more than 1000 fragments across the Siberian taiga.

The Sikhote-Alin meteorite fall occurred at 12.30 a.m. GMT on 12 February 1947 at latitude 46°9′ N and longitude 134°39′ E, about 375 kilometres from the Soviet port of Vladivostok. The majority of the meteorites landed in a wooded, undulating area just to the west of the Second Khanikheza River, covering an elliptical region about 2 kilometres long and 1 kilometre across. The fall was preceded by a brilliant fireball which flashed across a clear daylight sky and was, according to eyewitnesses, bright enough to cast shadows which swung around as it travelled. This was followed by a series of noises like distant explosions and by rumbling, roaring sounds. People living near the track of the fireball reported that cupboards flew open, window-panes blew out and objects fell from shelves as the ground trembled beneath their feet. Overhead the path of the fireball was marked by a dust trail in the atmosphere which took several hours to disperse.

Expeditions of local geologists and scientists from the Committee on Meteorites of the Soviet Academy of Sciences were sent to the region of the fall to conduct extensive investigations of the area. They found over 120 craters larger than half a metre across, and many separate meteorite fragments. The largest crater was 26 metres in diameter and 6 metres deep, and was surrounded by a ring of trees torn out by the roots. The fallen trees pointed radially outwards from the crater like the spokes of a bicycle wheel. The largest meteorite found weighed almost 1¾ tonnes, and several other pieces, each weighing more than a tonne, were recovered. Many of the smaller meteorites, weighing between 10 and several hundred kilograms, produced craters with diameters of a few metres or less.

Some of the meteorites were not found at the bottom of their respective craters, but at the end of tunnels which started near the centre of a crater and extended several metres into the soil. Others had formed a crater and then rebounded out again – one example weighed almost 200 kilograms and had jumped more than 5 metres from the 1½ metre. crater it formed on landing. A 13–kilogram meteorite embedded itself in a cedar tree and another, heavier, fragment chopped a growing fir tree in two. The general area of the fall was described by E. L. Krinov, the deputy head of the expedition, as being covered in pieces of splintered trees and stones thrown out of the craters, with considerable damage to the tops of more distant trees.

During a number of visits to the area over the next three years a total of about 23 tonnes of meteorites was recovered, either picked up from the surface or during excavation of the craters. The smallest piece weighed less than a fifth of a gram, measured 5 by 3 millimetres and was found lying on a fallen leaf. A number of the craters were left unexcavated and protective pavilions were built over three of them to preserve them as natural monuments. To complement the extensive ground investigations, aerial surveys were carried out from which detailed maps of the area of the fall were made.

From these studies scientists now have a reasonably clear picture of what happened over Siberia that winter day. A small member of the solar system, of principally metallic composition, entered the Earth's atmosphere at about 14.5 metres per second. After surviving until quite near the ground, the object finally disintegrated at a height of about 6 kilometres. Approximately 1000 nickel-iron meteorites, of various sizes and together weighing about 70 tonnes, were formed; these fell close together in the Sikhote-Alin area causing significant local damage, but no loss of life. Using the eyewitness accounts of over 300 people who saw the fireball, or the dust trail which marked the path of the object across the sky, it was even possible to estimate the orbit of the object before it struck the Earth.

Dramatic and devastating though it was, the fall of the Sikhote-Alin meteorite was not the largest such event to occur in the twentieth century. That honour belongs to an object – whose true nature remains controversial more than three-quarters of a century later – which fell in pre-revolutionary Russia on 30 June 1908.

For the peasant villagers living in the region of the Podkamennaia-Tunguska River, north of Lake Baikal and the city of Irkutsk in Siberia, the day probably began like any other. Then, a few minutes after seven o'clock in the morning, a brilliant daylight fireball, pale blue in colour, appeared in the southern sky. In a matter of seconds the object passed overhead, disappearing towards the north and leaving behind it a thick trail of dust suspended in the atmosphere. The fireball exploded at 7.14 a.m. local time, about six kilometres above a spot at 60° 55′ N latitude and 101° 57′ E longitude. According to eyewitnesses, the site of the explosion was marked by a column of flame and smoke which shot 20 kilometres into the sky and was visible from hundreds of kilometres away.

Following the disappearance of the fireball, there was a series of deafening explosions which were heard up to 1000 kilometres away. Along the track of the fireball there were reports of the ground shaking, crockery falling from shelves and window-panes cracking. At the town of Vanavara, about 60 kilometres south of the explosion, a witness sitting on his porch was thrown several metres and knocked unconscious. Many other people in the vicinity of the fall reported being knocked off their feet by the blastwave, or feeling a sensation of heat.

So great was the explosion that shockwaves were transmitted through the Earth's crust and recorded at the Irkutsk Magnetic and Meteorological Station 893 kilometres away. Russian scientists at the observatory detected seismic waves which began at 7.18 a.m. and continued for over an hour. About three-quarters of an hour after the explosion, the Irkutsk station also recorded the passage of the airwave, as the blast from the Tunguska event passed across the observatory. The blastwave continued on across Europe spreading outwards from the site of the explosion, and was registered on a recording barograph (a type of pressure-measuring instrument) at Potsdam near Berlin at 5.54 a.m. local time. It was also recorded a short time later at the South Kensington meteorological office and five other weather stations throughout England. Remarkably, a second pressure wave was detected at Potsdam the following day. This second wave was due to the shockfront which had travelled east from Tunguska and circumnavigated the world to reach Potsdam from the opposite direction 25 hours later.

The atmospheric wave was not the only effect of the Tunguska event which was detected across the continent. The following night was exceptionally bright throughout Europe and western Siberia, and in the south of Russia it was reportedly possible to read a newspaper at midnight without the help of artificial lights. This unusual sky brightness continued for several weeks, finally disappearing towards the end of August.

Despite the severity of the fall the intellectual climate in Russia at the time, combined with the extreme inaccessibility of the region in which it occurred, meant that it was almost 20 years before a scientific expedition to Tunguska was attempted.

Eventually, in 1927, L.A. Kulik led a group from the Soviet Academy of Sciences in search of the fallen meteorite. After battling across inhospitable terrain, Kulik and his expedition finally arrived at the site of the fall and gazed upon a scene of almost total devastation.

Within 30–40 kilometres of ground zero, the point immediately below the explosion, almost all the unprotected trees had been uprooted and blown flat. Only those sheltered by hills had escaped damage. An exception to this was at the very centre of the region of destruction, where some trees did remain standing but had been stripped of their branches and resembled a forest of blackened telegraph poles. Trees within the damaged area had also been scorched on the side facing the explosion, and this scorching could be traced out to 15–18 kilometres from the centre. The outer limit of the fallen trees was 52 kilometres from ground zero in one direction. Subsequent aerial surveys showed that the pattern of destruction was not circular but butterfly-shaped, and covered an area of approximately 4000 square kilometres.

From his written reports it is clear that Kulik was deeply affected by the devastation of the flattened and burned central area and by the sight of trees almost a metre thick snapped like twigs, their tops hurled tens of metres away. In the area where some trees remained upright, even walking about was quite hazardous because old dead trees, rotted through at the roots, were likely to fall at the slightest gust of wind.

At the centre of the affected region was a roughly circular depression about 8 kilometres across, bounded by a ring of small hills. The hills surrounding the marshy central depression were peppered by round holes several metres in diameter. Assuming that the holes were the craters of fallen meteorites the expedition, and subsequent ones, excavated them in a search for meteoritic debris, but without success. It was later found that the holes were natural formations unconnected with the explosion of the Tunguska object. Only in 1958, when a subsequent expedition searched the entire region of the fall, was evidence of extraterrestrial material discovered. This took the form of tiny spherules of iron and silicate material distributed amongst the soil. No large meteorite fragments were ever found.

The results of these investigations led the Soviet scientists to conclude that the original meteorite had struck the Earth at tremendous speed and was completely destroyed by the collision. Dust – all that remained of the solid body of the meteorite – was thrown into the atmosphere by the explosion, then spread around the world by stratospheric winds. It was this dust which, by reflecting sunlight around the world, was responsible for the bright nights observed for the next few weeks. The blast from the explosion flattened the trees and started fires which caused most of the damage to the forest. The lack of a crater was ascribed to the marshy nature of the ground in the region; the repeated winter freezing and summer thaw would destroy any sign of a crater within a few years. Surprisingly, the original researchers did not seem to consider that the terminal explosion had occurred above ground level.

An alternative explanation was proposed by the astronomer Fred Whipple. He suggested that the Tunguska object was not a stony meteorite but a small comet composed principally of ice and dust. Whipple pointed out that this would explain why, despite their efforts, the Soviet expeditions were unable to find any fragments larger than dust grains; if the object was indeed a comet, then there was nothing larger than dust in the first place. A comet would also explain why the object blew up in the atmosphere: its icy body would not be strong enough to survive until it reached the ground. The comet's tail, arriving later than the main body, was invoked to explain the dust which led to the unusual sky brightness over Europe.

Despite some rather more fanciful notions – the crash of an atomic-powered spaceship, or the sudden arrival of a mini black hole – the idea that the Tunguska event was caused by a comet has been popular for half a century, although recent work has come full circle and some astronomers are now returning to the theory that the object was a stony meteorite. They base this conclusion on the height of the terminal explosion, which occurred fairly low in the atmosphere – too low, it is argued, for the icy core of a comet to penetrate before being destroyed by atmospheric friction.

The absence of meteoritic debris at Tunguska is explained by the total energy of the object as it entered the atmosphere. With an estimated diameter of 100 metres, a mass of about 1,000,000 tonnes, and travelling at more than 10 metres per second relative to the Earth, the Tunguska object pushed its way through the atmosphere at hypersonic speed. Eventually the air in front of the object, unable to get out of the way fast enough, increased in pressure until it began to act like a solid wall. This sudden increase in drag brought the Tunguska object to a complete stop almost instantaneously, and its kinetic energy was liberated as a 12–megaton blast. The explosion pulverized the incoming object and distributed its remains – in the form of finely divided dust – in the atmosphere.

Whether caused by a comet or a meteorite, the explosion of the Tunguska object was many times the power of the weapons which destroyed the cities of Nagasaki and Hiroshima, and it is fortunate that it did not occur in a populated area. As civilization spreads inexorably across the surface of the world, the time may come when the Earth will not be so lucky.

The magnitude of the disaster which could befall a city struck by a large meteorite can be seen in the American state of Arizona. A short distance from US Highway 66 – about midway between the towns of Wimslow and Flagstaff and some 700 kilometres east of Los Angeles – is one of the most impressive natural formations on

Earth. The famous Barringer Crater, more than a kilometre in diameter, is the result of a cosmic impact about 50,000 years ago.

The crater was discovered in the 1870s as American settlers headed steadily westward. Originally called 'Coon Butte' or 'Coon Mountain', the apparently circular feature, with its raised rim, was visible for many miles across the flat landscape of Arizona and was originally believed to be the remains of an extinct volcano. The discovery of pieces of iron around the crater attracted the interest of prospectors, who took samples for analysis, and eventually Dr A.E. Foote, a mineralogist and meteorite collecter from Philadelphia, acquired one of these fragments. Realizing that the material was meteoritic iron, he travelled to Arizona in 1891 and collected over a hundred meteorites, the largest of which weighed 91 kilograms, from the area surrounding the crater. Despite his finds, and his failure to detect any evidence of vulcanism, Foote shied away from suggesting – at least in his paper published the same year by the American Association for the Advancement of Science – that the crater itself was formed by a meteorite. Foote may have suspected an impact origin for the crater but such a proposal was so contrary to the established geological thinking of the day that he seems to have been unwilling to suggest it himself in print.

Even excluding the possibility of an impact, origin opinions about the crater were diverse and often controversial, but most geologists of the time preferred to believe that it was an essentially terrestrial feature. In their view the discovery of meteoritic iron in the vicinity merely reflected a coincidental fall of meteorites in the same general area. This conclusion, although now known to be incorrect, was not unreasonable at the time since the craters on the Moon were generally believed to be of volcanic, not impact, origin. Ironically, Dr G.K. Gilbert, one of the leading geologists of the day and the director of the US Geological Survey, originally suspected that Coon Butte might be an impact crater but after visiting the site began to favour a more conventional explanation.

Then, in 1902, the existence of the crater came to the attention of Daniel Moreau Barringer, a mining engineer from Philadelphia. Barringer set out to examine Coon Butte and was sufficiently interested to negotiate the mining rights to the land in which the crater lay. Forming the Standard Iron Company to raise the necessary capital, Barringer studied the crater intensively for many years and confirmed that it was caused by the fall of a huge iron meteorite which he believed still lay buried beneath the surface. Examination of the small fragments of iron meteorite found around the crater showed that they contained traces of nickel, platinum and even small diamonds – so it seemed that the main body of the meteorite would be a great prize and Barringer's company spent considerable time and money drilling boreholes in search of it. Despite their efforts, and the outlay of around a quarter of a million dollars, Barringer never did find the core of the meteorite. Eventually the costs of mining became too high for his company and he was forced to abandon the search. He died, soon after, at home in Philadelphia.

Despite this failure, Barringer's work is now recognized as very important and in acknowledgment of his efforts the crater is now known as the Barringer Meteor Crater – a title which affords this entrepreneur and scientist a unique distinction. He is the only person to have craters named after him on two different worlds – there is also a Barringer crater on the Moon.

Today, Barringer's heirs have granted a long-term lease on the crater to another company which is exploiting the site as a tourist attraction. Visitors today, whether or not they know the details of its history, can examine a collection of meteorites in the musuem and then climb the 40–metre-high circular rim and gaze across the basin-shaped depression which dips more than 130 metres below the surrounding plain. From the rim the interior of the crater slopes sharply away for about 50 metres before it gradually levels out and merges into an almost flat central area. The height of the surrounding walls emphasizes the depth of the crater, and the general impression is simply breathtaking. It is difficult to grasp the scale of the opposite rim, more than a kilometre away, but what appear to be small outcrops of rock are in fact as large as two-storey houses. Around the crater, in all directions, is the debris thrown out by the original explosion, and many of the surrounding boulders are pitted by flying stones.

Paradoxically, although the crater seems circular when viewed from the rim, aerial photographs show that this is not the case.

When viewed from directly above, it appears almost square; only the corners are rounded and the sides are virtually straight. This non-circularity is not connected with the explosion of the meteorite but is due to the way in which the underlying rock fractured during the crater's formation.

Here in the Arizona desert is the youngest and best-preserved of the Earth's large meteorite craters but the passage of time, and its location in an already desolate part of the world, rob it of any menace. It is difficult to see in a human context, since it was formed well before the first men began to move into the area about 25,000 years ago. It is said that the Indians who inhabited the region invested the crater with great religious significance, and that their legends spoke of a god descending from heaven amidst fire before coming to rest below the ground, but few scientists would suggest that this indicates that humans actually witnessed the formation.

Despite its isolation, it is chilling to consider the formation of the Barringer Crater in the context of the fall at Tunguska, an event which occurred within living memory. The latest estimate of the mass of the Tunguska object is that it weighed between 1 and 10 million tonnes, roughly the same as the mass of the Barringer meteorite. Both objects are believed to have entered the Earth's atmosphere with a velocity of between 10 and 20 kilometres per second. The Tunguska meteor was of stony composition, not strong enough to survive the aerodynamic forces which it encountered during its passage through the atmosphere, and so exploded in flight. The Barringer object was composed of iron and nickel, which gave it the strength to penetrate more or less intact to the Earth's surface. Only once the object struck the ground was its enormous energy converted into heat, vaporizing the meteorite and much of the surrounding ground in a fraction of a second and causing the tremendous explosion which formed the crater. The energy of the blast in Arizona is believed to have been similar to that of the Tunguska event and, like Tunguska, resulted in the complete disruption of the meteorite. Barringer's search below the crater floor was doomed before it started; all that remained of the original object were the fragments of iron scattered across the Arizona desert.

COSMIC IMPACT

The realization that the formation of the Barringer Crater is an event of the same magnitude as Tunguska forces a new perspective on the physical size of the meteor crater. At a little over one kilometre in diameter it could comfortably enclose the entire village of Barwell, and is comparable in size to the shopping centres of many small towns. Since the region affected by the crater's formation must have been many times larger than the area of the crater itself, the scale of the disaster caused by the fall of a similar-sized meteorite into a populated area can be imagined. The impact and resulting explosion would devastate a small city, causing appalling loss of life and damage to property. Such a catastrophe would be many thousands of times worse than the destruction wrought by the atomic weapons which ended the Second World War.

2

The Violent Solar System

To understand these stones which fall so dramatically from the sky we must view them not individually but as members of the solar system. The correct perspective on these cosmic collisions is astronomical, not terrestrial. To appreciate this we must examine some of the other members of the Sun's family. Many of the planets and their moons show the scars of ancient impacts, and these are the clues to the history of the solar system. Only from them can we hope to understand the nature of the projectiles which strike the Earth today.

The Moon, Earth's only natural satellite, is the obvious place to start a survey of the solar system, because it is both close to home and well understood. Orbiting our planet at an average distance of 384,000 kilometres, the Moon is a world in its own right and yet, despite its closeness, it is fundamentally different from the Earth.

The Moon's diameter is 3476 kilometres, about one-quarter that of Earth, and its small size means that it is unable to retain an appreciable atmosphere. This has two important effects on the evolution of the lunar surface. Objects which encounter the Moon are not slowed by atmospheric friction and so crash directly on to its surface; and the absence of any weather, combined with geological inactivity, means that the appearance of the lunar surface changes extremely slowly.

Because the Moon is so close to the Earth, even the naked eye can see that it has two distinctly different types of terrain – the dark and light areas which make up the face of the Man in the Moon. A small telescope will show that the dark areas are fairly smooth, while the remainder of the lunar surface is mountainous and covered with craters of all sizes. The smoothness of the dark lunar plains misled early lunar cartographers into thinking that they were large bodies of water, so they have names beginning with the Latin words 'oceanus' or 'mare' (pl. 'maria'), which means sea. We now know that the lunar seas contain no water, but the original Latin names persist. Larger telescopes reveal that craters exist all over the Moon, but those in the maria are mostly much smaller than those in the lunar highlands.

Observations of the Moon reveal important facts about the history of cosmic bombardment in the solar system, and show that the majority of the large lunar craters are very old. This has been established by counting the number of craters in different regions of the Moon since, generally speaking, the parts with most craters are the oldest and those with least are the youngest. In practice this technique must be applied carefully, since once an area is heavily cratered the formation of new craters destroys some of the older ones, and debris thrown out by a new impact produces a rash of small craters nearby. (The formation of small craters by material thrown out during the formation of a larger one is known as secondary cratering.) None the less, after allowing for these effects it is clear that the smooth maria must be much younger than the lunar highlands, where the craters stand shoulder to shoulder.

The relative age of different parts of the Moon is clearly important, but to unravel the details of lunar evolution we must know the absolute age of at least some parts of the surface. Once this is established, the age of the rest of the Moon can be determined by crater counting. These ages can then be compared with those derived for other planets, and by piecing together all the clues provided by the craters we can reconstruct the early history of the solar system.

Analysis of lunar material brought back to Earth by Apollo astronauts has confirmed the view, held before the space age, that the smooth surfaces of the maria were caused by lava flowing out from below the Moon's crust. Samples from various different Apollo missions have also allowed the age of various parts of the lunar surface to be determined, and these show that the lunar maria, themselves the youngest parts of the Moon, are all over 3000 million years old.

Comparisons between the ancient heavily cratered lunar highlands and the smoother, younger maria are one of the keys to the study of the early solar system. The lava which flowed into the maria resurfaced large areas of the Moon, effectively resetting the crater-counting clock there to zero by obliterating all the original craters. Features visible in the maria today must have been formed after the lava solidified and, since this occurred between about 3200 and 3800 million years ago, we can see how the crater formation rate in the early solar system varied with time. There are about 30 times fewer craters in the maria compared with a similar area in the lunar highlands, so it is clear that there was an intense bombardment of the Moon early in its history, but that the rate of crater formation had already slowed dramatically by the time the lava flows began.

The shapes of the maria themselves provide another clue to the violent history of the Moon. Even a fairly cursory glance at a map will show that the maria are almost all of roughly circular outline. Obvious examples of this are the Mare Tranquillitatis, or Sea of Tranquillity, where the first Apollo mission landed, and the nearby Mare Serenitatis. A slightly longer look shows that the Mare Imbrium, the right eye of the Man in the Moon, would be circular but for the bite taken out of it by the poetically (if inaccurately) named Sinus Iridium, or Bay of Rainbows. Further consideration reveals that the shape of the Mare Imbrium is formed by two circular structures of different sizes lying one over the other.

The circularity of the lunar maria suggest that, like the normal lunar craters, they are of impact origin. The maria are, in effect, supercraters which filled with lava after they were formed. To distinguish between the original craters and the subsequent lava flows which filled them, the word 'maria' is now used to describe the smooth lava plains visible today, whilst the original super-craters, which may have been hundreds of kilometres across and 10 to 20 kilometres deep, are referred to as 'mare basins'. So the Mare Imbrium is the solidified lava lake which now fills the Imbrium basin. There are similar basins – about a dozen – on the far side of the Moon, but these have never been filled with lava.

Not long after the mare basins were formed, the interior of the Moon began to heat up as naturally occurring but short-lived radioactive isotopes decayed, releasing energy deep below the surface. This energy was unable to escape, so it melted the subsurface rock and molten material from below the crust seeped through the shattered rocks to fill the basins and solidify. The filling of the mare basins probably took about 800 million years – a calculation based on the range of ages derived from Apollo samples – and, although a few of the lava flows may be younger, the process was mostly complete by about 3100 million years ago. By then the Moon looked much as it does today, although some fairly well-known lunar craters did not yet exist. Soon after the lava flows solidified there was a brief, final, bombardment which formed a few large craters in the maria. Since then the Moon's appearance has hardly changed. About once every few million years an unusually large object crashes into the Moon and forms a major new crater; smaller craters continue to be formed by meteorite falls. High-resolution photography from spacecraft orbiting the Moon now makes it possible to use crater counting to estimate the rate at which these impacts have occurred over the last 100,000,000 years and, as we will see, this is in rough agreement with values derived from other sources.

Until recently the Moon was the only source of reliable cratering statistics, because the surface of the Earth is far too unstable to preserve any detail of events in the early solar system. The oldest known areas of the Earth's surface are about 3800 million years old, roughly the same age as the youngest areas of the lunar crust. All the older terrestrial rocks have long since been destroyed by geological activity. This means that our planet retains no record of the bombardment which occurred during the first thousand million years of its existence. Only now that unmanned spacecraft have returned the first images of the other planets, and the geography of more than a dozen new worlds has been revealed, is the violent history of the solar system becoming clear.

At the centre of the solar system is the Sun, one of about 100,000 million stars of various sizes and ages which make up the Milky Way galaxy. Although the Sun is classified by astronomers as a G-type dwarf there is nothing small about it; its diameter is about 1,400,000 kilometres. The mass of the Sun is about 330,000 times that of the Earth although its density, the amount of material in a given volume, is only about a quarter of the Earth's. Even so, to write the Sun's mass in tonnes requires a two followed by twenty-seven zeros, a figure which is more conveniently written as 2×10^{27} and usually spoken as two times ten to the twenty-seventh.

Like other stars, the Sun shines because deep below its surface nuclear reactions are taking place, liberating prodigious amounts of energy. The details of this process are beyond the scope of this book; we can simply say that near the centre of the Sun, where the temperature is about 10,000,000°C, hydrogen is being converted to helium; this actually destroys some of the Sun's mass and converts it to energy. The conversion occurs according to Einstein's famous equation $E = mc^2$, in which the symbol c represents the speed of light, m the mass destroyed and E the energy released.

The Sun is so massive (it contains more than 99 per cent of the total mass of the solar system) that it controls a family of planets stretching as far as lonely Pluto, which orbits the Sun at an average distance of 5900 million kilometres. Even at this tremendous distance, Pluto does not mark the end of the Sun's influence; many comets travel well beyond the planets, yet remain gravitationally controlled by the Sun. The exact distance at which the Sun loses its grip over the comets is uncertain, but it is probably about a thousand times farther away than Pluto, well on the way to the nearest star.

The planets themselves have always been a source of mystery. To the early watchers of the sky they were simply rather special stars which moved slowly about the heavens from night to night, and the word 'planet' derives from a Greek word meaning 'wanderer'. To people in an earlier and more poetic age, the planets' ability to move amongst the fixed stars indicated that they were of supreme importance, and they were named after powerful gods and goddesses. These names have survived the test of time and are still with us today.

Why the planets move – especially why they trace out their rather convoluted patterns in the sky – was a question that occupied the minds of philosophers for many centuries. Despite one or two dissenters who suggested that the Earth revolved around the Sun, the view of Aristotle (384–322 BC) that the Earth lay at the centre of an unchanging, spherical universe survived

27

until the Polish astronomer Nicolaus Copernicus revived the Sun-centred theory in his book *De Revolutionibus Orbium Coelestium* (On the Revolutions of the Heavenly Spheres) published in 1543. Copernicus's book raised an intellectual and theological storm which raged for decades until, in 1609, Johannes Kepler published the results of his work on planetary orbits. Kepler used the detailed naked-eye observations of the Danish astronomer Tycho Brahe and, after working for more than 20 years, developed a totally new concept in astronomical thinking. He suggested that the planets revolve around the Sun not in the circular orbits favoured by classical astronomers, but in elliptical ones.

A circle can be described as the path a point travels if it remains at the same distance from another fixed point. The fixed point is, of course, the centre and a line joining the centre to the edge, or circumference, is a radius. An ellipse – which looks like a squashed circle – is the path of something which moves so as to keep the sum of its distances from two fixed points constant. The two fixed points are known as the foci of the ellipse. If the foci of an ellipse are far apart the ellipse is long and thin and is said to be highly eccentric. If the foci are moved closer together the eccentricity is reduced and the ellipse gets rounder. If the two foci are placed one on top of each other the eccentricity is zero and the ellipse is just a normal circle.

Kepler's first law states that a planet moves around the Sun in an elliptical orbit with the Sun at one of the foci. This means that the distance of a planet from the Sun varies as it travels around its orbit. The closest point to the Sun is called the perihelion – which derives from 'helios', the Greek word for the Sun – and the furthest is called the aphelion. Fortunately, the eccentricity of the Earth's orbit, like that of most of the planets, is fairly small; therefore the distance to, and hence the total amount of heat received from, the Sun does not change appreciably during the course of a year.

Kepler also found that a planet moved more quickly when it was near perihelion than when it was farther away from the Sun. He expressed this in his second law, which states that during equal intervals of time the areas swept out by a line joining a planet to the Sun are the same. For planets, with their almost circular orbits, this is of little importance but for comets, which have highly eccentric orbits, it is much more significant. Kepler's third law states that the period of a planet's orbit squared is proportional to its mean distance from the Sun cubed.

Kepler's laws accurately describe the motion of a planet around the Sun in two dimensions, but reveal nothing about the three-dimensional structure of the solar system. The fact that the wanderings of the planets take place against a backdrop of a small number of constellations – the zodiac – which form a fairly narrow belt around the sky makes it possible to deduce that they all orbit the Sun in approximately the same plane. The plane of the Earth's orbit is known as the ecliptic and with the exception of Pluto, which is a highly unusual planet in many respects, the orbits of all the planets lie within about 7° of the ecliptic. Observations of the movements of the planets also reveal another highly significant fact: they all go round the Sun in the same direction – anticlockwise as viewed from above the north pole of the Sun. The majority of the natural satellites in the solar system also revolve around their respective planets in this direction; those which do not are generally small or unusual in other respects. Objects orbiting in the same sense as the rest of the planets are said to have prograde motion; the others are said to be in retrograde orbits.

With this general picture of the solar system, we can now investigate the planets and search for evidence of cosmic impacts on other worlds. Moving outwards from the Sun, the first planet is Mercury, which orbits the Sun at an average distance of 57.9 million kilometres. Known since prehistoric times, this tiny planet is named after the Roman messenger of the gods whose winged sandals allowed him to travel at great speed. In this respect Mercury is well named, since the planet completes one orbit of the Sun in just 88 Earth days, faster than any other sizable object in the solar system. With a diameter of 4878 kilometres – only about 40 per cent that of the Earth – Mercury is the smallest of the inner planets and not much larger than the Earth's Moon.

Mercury's small size and consequent low mass means that like the Moon it is unable to retain any appreciable atmosphere, and it is a barren world. Lacking any weather to help distribute the energy reaching the planet from the nearby Sun, Mercury is also a world of contrasting temperatures. The surface on the sunlit side may reach 430° C, higher than the melting point of lead, while the night side freezes more than 170°C below zero.

The proximity of Mercury to the Sun means that when viewed from the Earth it is usually seen low down near the horizon, either just before dawn or just after sunset. Observing conditions are poor near the horizon because turbulence in the atmosphere makes it difficult to get a steady image in a telescope, so it is impossible to study the planet in detail. These difficulties meant that little was known about Mercury until the American Mariner 10 spaceprobe flew past the planet on three separate occasions in 1974.

Mariner 10 photographs revealed that Mercury, like the Moon, is covered with impact craters. These range in size from tiny holes at the resolution limit of the spacecraft's television cameras to gigantic walled basins similar, but not identical, to those found on the Moon. Here and there are comparatively smooth plains, the origin of which is uncertain, but most of the surface is saturated by craters. Many of Mercury's craters are more than 100 kilometres across, but by far the most spectacular impact feature yet observed on the planet is the huge Caloris basin. Although this is the only one of its kind yet found on Mercury, it appears to be similar to the lunar mare basins and has several close relatives elsewhere in the solar system.

The Caloris basin is 1300 kilometres in diameter and surrounded by an almost circular ring of mountains about 2 kilometres high. To put this in perspective: Caloris is large enough to enclose both Britain and Ireland if they were miraculously transported to Mercury. Within the basin the floor is comparatively smooth, but does display a peculiar pattern of ridges which seem to take on almost geometrical patterns. Around the site of the basin are many secondary craters formed by debris hurled out by the original explosion. The impact which created the Caloris basin was a truly dramatic event and appears to have left its mark elsewhere on Mercury. On the opposite side of the planet is an area of humps and hillocks apparently thrown up by shockwaves from the impact which travelled through the planet and disrupted the antipodes. Geologists refer to this as chaotic or weird terrain.

Mercury exhibits other interesting geological phenomena, such as scarps hundreds of kilometres long which seem to be the result of the crust of the planet wrinkling as the core beneath it contracted. The details of these features need not concern us now, but they do reveal important information about the planet's evolution. Some of these formations have survived for several thousand million years, so it is clear that Mercury is no longer geologically active, and the surface which we see today is very old. The scars of impact craters which cover Mercury date from a time not long after the planet formed. From the evidence of crater counting on the moon this period seems to have occurred about 4000 million years ago, so Mercury's surface offers a glimpse of events in the very distant past.

Continuing outwards, we encounter the planet Venus which, at about 108 million kilometres from the Sun, lies roughly midway between Mercury and the Earth. Similiar in size to the Earth, Venus was once thought to be our planet's twin sister, and many people believed for a time that it was the abode of some sort of life. This romantic notion was encouraged by the fact that Venus has an atmosphere, permanently hiding its surface below a sea of clouds. Astronomers once believed these clouds were due to water vapour, and some pictured a world covered in swamps and populated by creatures similar to the amphibious dinosaurs once found on the Earth. Perhaps sadly, ground- and space-based observations in the 1960s revealed that the surface of Venus is at a temperature of 500° C, and that the pressure at the surface exceeds 90 Earth atmospheres. Even more damaging to the hopes of finding a habitable planet was the revelation that the clouds of Venus are not water, but droplets of sulphuric acid. Venus, as more than one astronomer has remarked, closely resembles the classical vision of hell.

Although hidden beneath its clouds, the surface of Venus can be probed by radar, either from orbiting spacecraft or from large ground-based radio telescopes. Both these techniques have now been used to make radar maps of Venus. The resolution of these maps is too poor to show much small-scale detail, but they have allowed us to investigate the general nature of the Venusian surface. It is clear that Venus is still geologically active and preserves little or no record of major cosmic impacts. Only when more detailed radar maps, capable of resolving much smaller features on the surface of the planet, are available is there any chance its collision record might be revealed.

Beyond Venus lies the Earth, and beyond that is the red planet Mars. Once thought to be the home of advanced alien beings but now believed to be lifeless, Mars is larger than the Moon but smaller than the Earth. It orbits 228,000,000 kilometres or so from the Sun, taking about two Earth years for each revolution. Like the Moon, Mars has many thousands of impact craters but, like the Earth, it is still geologically active and has an atmosphere. The craters have survived because the present Martian atmosphere is too thin to allow liquid water on the planet, so the processes of erosion are slow compared with those on the Earth. Accordingly, the Martian surface retains many of its ancient craters, only slightly subdued by the passage of time. Despite this, smaller craters are far fewer on Mars than on the Moon, because many have been obliterated by dust storms and lie buried beneath the fine Martian sand.

The geology of Mars is fascinating, for it is a planet of major contrasts. The southern hemisphere is old and heavily cratered, but the northern contains smooth plains and huge volcanoes. Despite the lack of water today the planet has many features which point to the existence of water in the past – dried-up rivers and huge areas which appear to have been flooded quite recently. The water which once flowed across these regions is probably now locked up in the Martian polar caps, or in permanently frozen soil beneath the surface. Finally there is the 5000–kilometre-long Mariner Valley, which cuts across the surface and resembles an attempt to start the process of continental drift which somehow failed at birth.

These very features which make the planet so interesting complicate the study of its history, because it is clear that the surface of Mars is slowly changing, erasing the clues to its past. It is evident from the presence of crater-saturated terrain in the south that, like the Moon and Mercury, Mars was once subjected to an intense bombardment; and equally obvious from the smooth terrain in the north that the crater-forming epoch ended a long time ago. Unfortunately, dating these different periods of Martian history is hampered by the gradual erosion of the craters and the lack of any Martian soil for laboratory analysis. It is, however, clear that Mars did not escape the catastrophic collisions which formed the lunar maria and the Caloris basin on Mercury, because the planet boasts several large impact basins. The two largest were named by telescopic observers many years before their true nature was determined, and are known as Hellas and Argyre. Photographs taken by unmanned spacecraft have revealed that the Hellas basin is about 5 kilometres deep and 1600 kilometres in diameter, and the Argyre basin is about two-thirds this size.

From the orbit of Mars to the giant planet Jupiter is 550,000,000 kilometres – more than twice the distance which separates Mars from the Sun. The enormous gulf of space between these two planets is not, however, entirely empty; it contains the thousands of tiny worlds which make up the asteroid belt. The rocky asteroids mark an important transition: the change from the small Earth-like planets to the frozen gas giants of the outer solar system. Once at Jupiter we enter a region of huge planets with enormous distances between them.

Jupiter is almost unbelievably large and, although it has a mass 318 times that of the Earth, it spins on its axis in only ten hours. Jupiter outweighs all the other planets put together, and this size gives it a gravitational field capable of controlling more than a dozen moons, affecting the orbits of objects in the asteroid belt and capturing a family of comets. Like the Sun, Jupiter is composed principally of hydrogen and helium, and has no observable solid surface. The banded appearance which makes the planet such an interesting sight in a small telescope is simply a view of the top cloud layers of the dense atmosphere, swept along lines of latitude by Jupiter's rapid rotation. This turbulent and constantly changing atmosphere cannot retain the imprints of colliding objects, so to learn something of cosmic impacts in the Jupiter system we must survey the surfaces of the Jovian moons which, at least superficially, resemble those of the familiar terrestrial planets.

Jupiter has over a dozen satellites, some of which orbit over 20,000,000 kilometres from the planet. They range in size from the four planet-sized moons discovered by Galileo in 1610 to a number of smaller objects found telescopically from the Earth during this century. Several small satellites were also discovered in photographs taken by the American Voyager spacecraft as it flew past Jupiter in 1979. Little is known of the outer satellites except that they are small, mostly less than 100 kilometres across, and have fairly elliptical orbits. The outermost four of these tiny moons, which go around Jupiter the opposite way to all the others, orbit so far from the planet that they are influenced by the gravity of the other planets and are unstable. One day they will all escape from Jupiter's grasp, but they will doubtless be replaced by others captured from the asteroid belt.

Four of the other small Jovian moons make up an interesting little group of their own. They all orbit the planet at an average distance of about 11,000,000 kilometres and their orbits are all inclined at about 28° to Jupiter's equator. This orbital similarity suggests that they are the fragments of a single object, shattered at some time in the remote past. Since they are too far from Jupiter to have been disrupted by the planet's gravitational field, the most likely cause of such a break-up is a collision – perhaps between an icy moon and a comet passing through the Jovian system.

With the exception of the irregular satellite Amalthea, the five innermost satellites are all comparable in size to the Earth's Moon. The largest two, Ganymede and Callisto, are actually bigger than Mercury and, were they to be found elsewhere in the solar system, would be regarded as planets in their own right. Until the Voyager missions even these satellites were almost totally unknown territory. Then, in a few fantastic weeks during 1979, the two Voyager spacecraft transformed them into individual landscapes of incredible complexity.

Io, the smallest of the four Galilean moons, was found to be surprisingly crater-free when the first photographs from Voyager 1 were received on Earth. As the spacecraft drew closer, and the detail in the pictures increased, the reason for this became clear. Io has a number of active volcanoes and these smooth over its surface with outpourings of sulphur-rich lava, covering over any craters almost as quickly as they are formed. Although Io's precise age is difficult to ascertain, its surface is one of the youngest in the solar system and so preserves no evidence of its history. Io cannot provide any clues to the nature of the objects which fall on Earth, so we will pass by this otherwise fascinating world.

Europa, the next satellite out from Jupiter, is also virtually craterless but the reason for this is quite different. Io is a world of active volcanoes; Europa is a world of ice. Detailed photographs from the Voyager spacecraft show that Europa's surface is uncannily smooth; almost the only relief is a complex pattern of grooves which crisscross the surface. These grooves, which make Europa resemble a map of the fabled Martian canals, are only a few hundred metres deep, but they are tens of kilometres wide and thousands of kilometres long. Extensive searches of Europa have revealed only a small number of craters and this suggests that, as on Io, some process is removing them almost as quickly as they are formed. The key to this process is found in Europa's low density, which suggests that there is a large quantity of water locked up beneath the surface. The crust seems to be a mixture of ice and dust up to 100 kilometres thick.

This icy crust explains Europa's overall smoothness. The crust is not strong enough to support the weight of mountains, and impact craters on the surface are soon healed by fresh ice from the moon's interior. On the strength of the few craters which can be seen, the age of the Europan crust is estimated to be about the same as that of the lunar maria, but this is highly uncertain. Like Jupiter and Io, Europa can reveal very little about cratering processes in the solar system.

Only at Ganymede, third of the Galilean moons, is there evidence of ancient cratered terrain. Here too are large impact basins similar, but not identical, to those on the inner planets. One important difference is that the large impact basins on Ganymede are often surrounded by a series of concentric rings, like the ripples formed on a pond when a stone is thrown into the water. These rings show that the crust is icy, and when shockwaves spread from the site of an impact they are almost literally frozen into the ground. Unfortunately the circular structures surrounding the largest of the impact basins have been partly removed by subsequent modification of the surface, and only fragments of the original circular features remain. This makes the study of the basins more difficult, but it does indicate that they must be extremely old. Crater-counting techniques, using the cratering rates established for the lunar surface, indicate that some of Ganymede's surface is between three and three and a half billion years old.

It may seem that Jupiter and its moons are fascinating in their own right, but unable to provide many clues to the history of the early solar system. This is true of the innermost moons, but certainly not of the last of the four Galilean moons, Callisto. Even a cursory glance at Callisto reveals that much of its surface is saturated with craters and that, unlike any of the solar system's other solid worlds, Callisto has virtually no young smooth plains. It is almost certainly the system's most heavily cratered world.

The only parts of Callisto not completely dominated by craters are a few smooth circular areas which, as closer examination shows, are surrounded by the sort of concentric rings seen on Ganymede. These smooth areas are themselves impact features, the remains of huge craters similar to the very large basins on Mercury, the Moon and Mars. The largest of these, Valhalla, is 300 kilometres across and is surrounded by a ring system which stretches 3000 kilometres across the surface, dominating one hemisphere.

From the craters it is clear that Callisto is a world whose geological evolution stopped almost before it began. The surface has remained essentially unchanged since it was formed, making it not merely the roughest, but also probably the oldest surface in the solar system. Written somewhere in the pattern of craters on this frozen and battered world is much of the system's history.

Beyond the diverse and enigmatic moons of Jupiter lies another vast tract of empty space, occupied by only a few asteroids and comets pursuing their lonely paths around the Sun. It is more than 500,000,000 kilometres from Jupiter to the next major planet, Saturn.

Although Saturn is distinguished from all the other planets by its bright system of rings, in many respects it closely resembles Jupiter. Like Jupiter, it is a gas giant planet many times larger than the Earth which masks its interior beneath a permanent veil of banded clouds and, as with Jupiter, it is not the planet but the moons of Saturn that are the key to determining the processes which occurred in the early solar system. Saturn has an extensive satellite system, the true complexity of which was finally revealed by measurements made by the Voyager spacecraft in 1980 and 1981.

Saturn's largest moon, Titan, has a diameter of 5000 kilometres, which makes it slightly larger than Mercury. This suggests that its surface might reveal some evidence of its history, but unfortunately this is not the case. Titan has an atmosphere which, like the clouds of Venus, totally obscures the surface from view. Voyager measurements suggest that the atmosphere contains a complex mixture of chemicals and may even contain the building blocks of biological systems, although on a frozen world so far from the Sun it is unlikely that these could ever develop into life. Titan is fascinating, but while it hides its surface beneath an impenetrable cloud layer we must pass it by.

Apart from Titan, Saturn has a further eight well-known moons which range in diameter from 150 to 1500 kilometres, making them all much smaller than the four main moons of Jupiter. Like the Jovian moons, the satellites of Saturn are all of low density and consist of a mixture of ice and rock. The Saturnian moons show no sign of volcanic activity, but their surfaces do bear witness to some dramatic events in the distant past.

The innermost of these satellites is Mimas, one of the smaller moons, with a diameter of only 350 kilometres. Mimas orbits about 40,000 kilometres farther from Saturn than the outermost of the planet's three main rings. Little is known about it except that its density is very low and much of its surface is heavily cratered and therefore very old. What makes Mimas of particular interest is the discovery that one hemisphere is dominated by a huge crater 130 kilometres across and 9 kilometres deep. This gigantic cavity is more than a quarter of the diameter of Mimas, and the colossal impact which formed it must have come close to destroying this icy world completely. In view of the long-held belief that the rings of Saturn are the remains of a shattered moon, it is tempting to speculate that a nearby companion of Mimas was not lucky enough to escape the consequences of a cosmic impact.

Orbiting 60,000 kilometres beyond Mimas is Enceladus, an icy moon almost the same size as its neighbour. Enceladus has a fairly smooth surface, probably because of partial crust resurfacing. Enceladus is much too small to have a molten core like the Earth, and the energy for this resurfacing comes from tidal forces caused by the gravitational tug of war between Saturn pulling in one direction while the attraction from the next two moons, Tethys and Dione, pulls the other way. This friction is enough to warm the interior of Enceladus slightly and to generate enough geological activity to smooth out the surface, destroying any evidence of ancient cosmic impacts.

Nearby Tethys, which has a diameter of just over 1000 kilometres, is quite heavily cratered but its surface is dominated by an unusual trench 750 kilometres long and 60 kilometres wide. This huge scar may be caused by geological faulting or a collision which, like the impact on Mimas, came close to shattering the moon in the distant past. This idea is supported by the discovery of a large circular feature on the opposite side of Tethys which may be the remains of a crater over 100 kilometres in diameter. Dione, next satellite out from Saturn and near neighbour of Tethys, is also about 1000 kilometres in diameter, but displays none of the dramatic impact features of its companions. Dione has many thousands of craters, but none so large as to suggest that the moon ever came close to total destruction.

After Dione come the two largest moons, Rhea and Titan. Rhea is heavily cratered and much of its surface, like that of Callisto, is crater-saturated. Rhea may rival Callisto in possessing the oldest preserved crust of any object in the solar system. Comparison of the cratering experienced by these two ancient surfaces may provide important clues about how the planet-building process varied with increasing distance from the Sun. This is vital to our understanding of how the solar system was formed.

Beyond Rhea and cloud-wrapped Titan lie three unusual worlds: Hyperion, Iapetus and Phoebe. Ground-based astronomers deduced some years ago that Hyperion was fairly small, but Voyager photographs revealed that it was also highly irregular and heavily cratered. Voyager showed that the dimensions of Hyperion were approximately 400 by 250 by 250 kilometres, and that its long axis does not point towards Saturn. This is unusal. Hyperion would be expected to point towards Saturn because of an effect known as gravity-gradient stabilization. Its gravitational instability may indicate that at some time in the past it was struck by another large object and has not yet settled down. Further studies of the gravitational effects of Saturn on Hyperion are required to confirm this suggestion.

Iapetus, unlike Hyperion, is large enough to be circular and shows no sign of any dramatic impact features, although it does boast at least one crater in the 200–kilometre class. Almost nothing is known about Phoebe except that it is small and orbits over 14,000,000 kilometres from Saturn. This enormous distance – with the fact that like the outer moons of Jupiter, Phoebe goes around Saturn in a retrograde orbit – suggests that it is a captured asteroid, and only a temporary member of Saturn's family.

The history of Saturn's moons has been exceptionally violent. Nowhere else in the solar system is there so much evidence of collisions on such a world-shattering scale. The smaller moons discovered orbiting Saturn in the last few years by both ground-based studies and by the Voyagers also suggest an extremely turbulent past. Several of them orbit very close to Saturn's magnificent ring system, boosting belief in the idea that the rings themselves are the debris of an icy inner moon. Two of these newly discovered objects, known at present simply as S10 and S11, actually have orbits around Saturn whose radii differ by less than 50 kilometres. This is less than the diameter of either object, so at first sight it appears that they must collide when the faster-moving inner moon catches up and overtakes its twin. In fact this does not happen, because a complex gravitational interaction causes the two moons to exchange orbits and thus avoid destruction. It is highly unlikely that such a complicated orbital situation arose by chance, and most astronomers believe that S10 and S11 are two fragments of a single body split assunder by a collision similar to the one which produced the giant crater on Mimas.

From Saturn it is another 1,400,000,000 kilometres to the next planet, the fascinating world of Uranus. Uranus is a gas planet rather smaller than the giant planets Jupiter and Saturn, and probably consists of a rocky core overlaid by a thick sheet of ice, topped by a dense atmosphere. Although this thick blanket of clouds hides the surface of the planet, there is plenty of evidence that Uranus has had a violent past.

It has been known for many years that the planet's axis of rotation is tipped 97° from the plane of its orbit, so it appears to roll around the Sun on its side, but measurements from the American Voyager 2 spacecraft have shown that the magnetic poles of Uranus are displaced by a staggering 55° from the geographic poles. Scientists are still trying to explain this amazing discovery. One possibility is that Uranus was once struck by an object at least as large as the Earth, and the collision tipped the planet on to its side, displacing the magnetic pole in the process. This suggestion is only one of a number of ideas on how Uranus developed this unusual arrangement, and it may be years before astronomers really understand whether a cosmic impact was responsible for toppling the planet.

Uranus is also encircled by a number of narrow and very dark rings. The first of these were discovered from Earth in 1977, and before Voyager 2 flew past Uranus in January 1986 a total of nine were known. Voyager measurements suggest that there are many other rings, or parts of rings, but it is not clear how they were formed. Voyager 2 also discovered a number of small Uranian moons, some of which may help to keep the material making up the rings in the correct orbits.

Of the five satellites known before the Voyager encounter, all have densities in the range 1.5–1.7 grams per cubic centimetre and are probably a mixture of rock and ice. The four largest moons – Ariel, Umbriel, Titania and Oberon – are all between 1000 and 1600 kilometres in diameter and greyish in colour. There are several large craters amongst these moons and Titania, the largest, has examples 200 and 300 kilometres in diameter. Titania also boasts 1500–kilometre-long faults, up to 75 kilometres wide, cutting across what seems to be a heavily cratered and very ancient surface.

By far the strangest of the five main satellites is undoubtedly the innermost moon, Miranda. Although only about 500 kilometres in diameter, Miranda seems to have a collection of the most bizarre features seen anywhere in the solar system. Voyager 2 pictures revealed craters, valleys like those of Mars, unusual fault patterns similar to those found on Mercury, grooved terrain like that found on Jupiter's moon Ganymede, and a unique region like a pile of pancakes placed one on top of another. Astronomers and geologists trying to explain these features have suggested that Miranda was once smashed to pieces in a collision and gradually reassembled itself. Heat released during this reassembly might have provided the energy to produce the flows and other strange landforms which mark this tiny world.

Uranus marks a frontier in the solar system, for although several spacecraft have travelled on into interplanetary space, none has flown anywhere near Neptune or Pluto and no detailed information is available on either of these distant worlds. Conventional astronomical techniques have revealed enough to show that at the fringes of the solar system there is evidence for cataclysmic events on a scale that may dwarf the destruction of some of Saturn's moons.

Neptune is a gas giant planet similar in many respects to Uranus and, as with the other giant worlds, the key to its strangeness is in its satellites. Neptune has only two known moons, but they are both highly unusual. The innermost, Triton, has a diameter of around 6000 kilometres and is probably the largest satellite in the solar system. Triton is in a retrograde, circular orbit very close to the planet and inclined at 20° to Neptune's equator. Satellites in highly inclined, retrograde orbits are usually captured asteroids but Triton is far too large to be described in this way, and its origin is a mystery. The second moon, Nereid, is only about 500 kilometres in diameter and in a prograde but highly eccentric orbit which ranges from 1.6 to 9.6 million kilometres from the planet.

Something very dramatic seems to have occurred in Neptune's past to produce this strange orbital arrangement, and it was once believed that whatever disrupted the Neptunian system may have been connected with the unusual axial tilt of Uranus and the origin

41

of the outermost planet, Pluto. This idea came about because Pluto is in an eccentric and highly inclined orbit which actually brings it inside the orbit of Neptune at regular intervals, and for a time it did appear possible that Pluto might be an escaped satellite of Neptune. Certainly, with a diameter of only a few thousand kilometres, Pluto is about the right size for such a satellite and it was suggested that a cataclysm had swept the outer planets, toppling Uranus on to its side and disrupting Neptune's satellites. Unfortunately, the discovery (in 1978) that Pluto has a satellite almost certainly rules out any connection, since it is difficult to imagine how Pluto could have escaped from Neptune and yet retained a moon of its own.

Pluto and its icy satellite Charon are now believed to be small worlds, not much larger than some of the asteroids and quite unlike any of the other planets. Their true nature remains mysterious, and it is likely to be many decades before detailed photographs will reveal their secrets. Presumably they formed here on the fringes of the solar system many millions of years ago and have remained in deep freeze ever since – the system's lonely outer markers.

Strictly speaking, Pluto is not the edge of the Sun's domain, for our star's influence stretches well beyond the orbit of the outermost planet, but the exact boundary between solar and interstellar space is of no concern to us at present. We have travelled from the warm heart of the solar system to its icy perimeter and seen evidence for massive impacts at almost every stage of our journey. From the size of the craters it is clear that some were caused by impacts of objects many tens, if not hundreds, of kilometres in size. Crater counting suggests that most – but not all – these impacts occurred many thousands of millions of years ago. What can they tell us about the formation and evolution of the solar system and about the future risk of cosmic impacts on Earth?

3

Cosmic Debris

The evidence from the planets, combined with advances in astronomy, has now provided a fairly clear picture of the way in which the solar system was formed. The first step was taken in one of the clouds of gas and dust which pervade the space between the stars. These clouds, which are many thousands of times more massive than a single star, exist in huge numbers throughout the galaxy, and under normal circumstances are fairly stable. The solar system began when – for some as yet unexplained reason – one such cloud was compressed, setting up turbulence which increased the density of some of its parts. This in turn produced regions of increased gravitational attraction, which drew in more of the surrounding gas and dust. The extra material increased the gravitational influence of the condensations still further and attracted in yet more material, starting a gradual but virtually unstoppable disintegration of the cloud into a number of cloudlets. As the cloud fragmented, each cloudlet continued its own inexorable, and gradually accelerating, collapse.

Eventually the cloud which was to become the Sun began to warm up, as material falling in towards the centre collided with the gas and dust already there and the energy given up by the infalling material was released as heat. While the cloud – usually called the solar nebula – was diffuse this energy could radiate back into space; but as more material was attracted in, and the cloud became more and more dense, the heat found it increasingly difficult to escape. Soon the density and temperature of the solar nebula's central regions began to rise rapidly and the core became hot enough to emit light. The first stage of starbirth was complete, but the newly formed Sun was still contracting under the influence of gravity.

After undergoing a series of spectacular pulsations, the outward pressure from the hot gas began to balance the gravitational forces and the Sun settled down into a fairly stable condition. By now the centre was hot enough for nuclear reactions to start and the Sun began to obtain its energy from the fusion of hydrogen atoms into helium, an energy source sufficient to last for about 10 thousand million years. The Sun now entered into middle age, and began to develop a family.

The planets were formed because not all the material from the collapsing cloudlet had managed to reach the centre of the solar nebula before the Sun switched on, and a considerable quantity of gas and dust remained around the new star. Since the fragmentation of the original interstellar cloud into cloudlets almost certainly introduced some turbulence, the inner regions of the solar nebula were rotating during the formation of the Sun. This rotation was eventually distributed between the Sun and the orbiting gas and dust, and as part of this process the orbiting material settled down to form a disc rotating about the Sun, roughly parallel to the solar equator.

During the final stages of the collapse the heat from the forming Sun warmed the surrounding material, driving most of the gases away from the centre of the solar nebula. Only material capable of surviving at high temperatures could remain close to the Sun; almost all the lighter elements were boiled away. Farther out, where temperatures remained low, increasing amounts of gas and icy material from the original interstellar cloud remained. Gradually, individual grains in the orbiting material began to collide and stick together and, in a process which mimicked the formation of the Sun itself, the clumps began to collapse under their mutual gravitational attraction. Soon the Sun was surrounded by a swarm of mini-planets, or planetesimals, each trying to grow by sweeping up its neighbours. Near the Sun the planetesimals were dominated by stony and metallic elements; farther out they were little more than giant snowballs of frozen gases mixed with small amounts of dust. Eventually each region of the proto-planetary disc contained a few large objects, each sweeping up its smaller neighbours. The planet-building process – known as accretion – had begun in earnest.

Close in to the Sun, where the rocky planets formed, their surfaces recorded the final stages of the accretion process in the form of craters. The huge basins in the inner solar system were formed when planetesimals tens or hundreds of kilometres across crashed into the still-growing planets, obliterating huge areas of crust and hurling debris in all directions. Only once the majority of these large objects had been removed did the planets begin to develop the features observed today. From the ages of meteorites believed to be material left over from accretion, and from the crater-counting studies of the Moon and planets, we know that the final stage of planet-building occurred between 4.5 and 3.9 thousand million years ago..

Farther from the Sun, where the orbiting material was dominated by frozen gas and ices, the planets developed in a similar fashion. Here, though, instead of rocky worlds, gas giant planets like Jupiter and Saturn were formed. Here too were formed the small, icy objects which became the moons of the outer planets – frozen worlds like Titania, Callisto and Rhea. The surfaces of these satellites, like those of the inner planets, recorded the final stages of their formation as giant impact craters.

Still farther away, in the outer reaches of the solar nebula, the final stages of accretion did not occur. Perhaps because of the disturbing influences of nearby stars, or simply the enormous volume of space involved, no planets formed. Instead, the space beyond Pluto was filled with a thousand billion or more icy planetesimals, each a few kilometres in diameter – the frozen remnants of the original solar nebula. Too faint to be seen from Earth, these snowballs make up the reservoir of comets known as the Oort cloud. Only a tiny fraction of them ever leave the Oort cloud and approach the Sun close enough to sweep across the orbits of the planets and become visible from Earth.

Although many of the fine details remain to be worked out, this scheme seems to explain most of the features of the planets as we see them today. In particular it explains why the inner planets are small and rocky while the giant outer worlds are composed almost entirely of gas, and why so many large impacts seem to have occurred about 4000 million years ago. It can also resolve one of the mysteries which puzzled astronomers of the nineteenth century – the existence of a family of tiny planets between Mars and Jupiter: the asteroid belt.

The story of the asteroids goes back to the year 1772 when a little-known German professor of mathematics pointed out an interesting relationship connecting the orbits of the planets. Johann Daniel Titius noticed that if the number 4 is added to each of the numbers in the series 0, 3, 6, 12, 24, 48, 96 – in which, apart from the second, each number is double the preceding one – the resulting values are in remarkable agreement with the ratios of the distance of each planet from the Sun. In fact if the numbers in Titius's series were divided by 10, and the distance from the Earth to the Sun was taken to be equal to 1, then the resulting sequence – apart from the value of 2.8, for which no planet was then known – was almost exactly correct as far as Saturn, then thought to be the most distant planet.

Setting the distance from the Earth to the Sun at equal to 1 might seem a rather illogical thing to do, but it is in fact a convenient astronomical convention and the Earth–Sun distance of 149.6 million kilometres is known as an astronomical unit – usually abbreviated to AU. The use of astronomical units to describe distances in the solar system has two immediate advantages. Firstly, it makes the numbers a lot easier to handle because it disposes of all the zeros needed to express the distances in kilometres. Secondly, according to Kepler's third law, the time taken for a planet to orbit the Sun in years is simply its average distance from the Sun in astronomical units raised to the power 3/2.

The accuracy of Titius's rule (shown in Table 3.1) so impressed the German astronomer Johann Bode (1747–1826) that he included it in a book published in 1772 and it became known as Bode's Law. To redress this minor injustice, modern astronomers prefer to divide the credit for the discovery and refer to the Titius-Bode Law.

Although the Titius-Bode sequence is certainly interesting, a scientific theory should not merely describe something but should actually make predictions, which can then be tested by further observations or experiments. Accordingly the discovery – by William Herschel in 1781 – of the planet Uranus at almost exactly the predicted distance provided a spectacular boost for the Titius-Bode Law. In fact Uranus orbits the Sun at a mean distance of 19.2 astronomical units compared with the predicted value of 19.6 AU, so the agreement is remarkably good.

TABLE 3.1

Planet	Titius Series Value	Distance from Sun in AU
Mercury	0.4	0.39
Venus	0.7	0.72
Earth	1.0	1.00
Mars	1.6	1.52
—	2.8	—
Jupiter	5.2	5.20
Saturn	9.6	9.54

The apparent success of the Titius-Bode Law in predicting the distance of Uranus from the Sun concentrated attention on the missing planet which the rule suggested should be orbiting at 2.8 AU. In particular a German astronomer, Baron Xaver von Zach, reasoned that if such a planet did exist it would have to be very faint to have avoided discovery so long. Accordingly, if the missing planet was to be found it would require a diligent search. The best hope seemed to be to use a telescope to sweep the sky and try to find a faint object which changed its position from night to night. Since this was well before the advent of astronomical photography, the only method available to von Zach was to sketch a number of different parts of the sky as often as possible and, by comparing drawings made a few days apart, try to detect something that had moved between the dates of the two drawings.

Unfortunately, the area of sky visible through a telescope is very small and this, combined with the time needed to make the necessary sketches, meant that it would be a hopeless task for one man to attempt to search the whole sky in this way. Even though the area of sky to be searched could be restricted to a zone near the ecliptic plane – for that is where the missng planet was expected to lie – the search area still covered many hundreds of square degrees, so von Zach decided to recruit other observers. In September 1800 he arranged a meeting with five other German astronomers at the observatory belonging to the famous lunar observer Johann Schroter and suggested that each of them begin to search a separate region of sky for the missing planet. In the meantime von Zach undertook to seek more volunteers for the group, who gave themselves the nickname of the 'celestial police'.

Von Zach's approach was certainly sound, and without doubt would eventually have produced results, but by a cruel stroke of fate the celestial police were to be denied the reward of discovering the missing planet. This honour fell to an Italian astronomer, Giuseppe Piazza, who was mapping a region of sky near the constellation of Taurus, the Bull. On 1 January 1801, the first day of the nineteenth century, he noticed a faint star which seemed to move from night to night.

Piazza, who was not looking for the missing planet, first believed that he had discovered a faint comet, echoing the mistake made by Herschel when he first observed Uranus. Piazza followed the object's motion until early February, when he was taken ill and had to stop observing for a time. Unfortunately, by the time his letters announcing the find had reached other astronomers, the new object had moved into the evening twilight and was no longer observable. This caused some dismay in the astronomical world, since no method then existed to calculate the orbit of the new body from Piazza's observations, and it was quite likely that by the time it moved back into a dark sky its position would be so uncertain that it would be impossible to find.

Fortunately a young German mathematician, Carl Friedrich Gauss, had recently devised a new method of orbit computation. Using this he was able to calculate where the object would be found when it reappeared from behind the Sun. With these predictions, the new planet was relocated almost exactly a year after the original discovery and, with its existence confirmed, was named Ceres, after the mother goddess of Sicily. The distance of Ceres from the Sun was determined to be 2.77 AU, fitting the Titius–Bode Law prediction of 2.8 AU almost exactly.

There the matter of the missing planet would probably have rested had not Heinrich Olbers, one of the original celestial police, found another moving star in the same region of sky a few months later. The second object, also found to orbit the Sun at about 2.8 AU, was named Pallas and provided the first clue that the space between Mars and Jupiter might contain a number of small planets

48

rather than one large one. Within five years two more of these tiny worlds were discovered: the third, Juno, by Karl Ludwig Harding in 1804 and the fourth, Vesta, by Olbers in 1807. The small size of these four objects (even the largest, Ceres, is only about 1000 kilometres in diameter) meant that they did not show a perceptible disc when viewed through a telescope and they became known as asteroids, a word derived from a Greek expression meaning 'starlike'. Today the asteroids are officially designated minor planets and given a number as well as a name by the International Astronomical Union.

Despite further searches it was almost 40 years before another asteroid was discovered. K.L. Henke found asteroid 5 Astrea in 1846 and followed this success a couple of years later by finding 6 Hebe. Over the next few decades more and more asteroids were discovered until by 1890 over 300 had been found. Then, in 1891, Max Wolf of the Heidelberg Observatory began to use astronomical photography in the search, and the rate of discovery increased dramatically. Wolf took long-exposure photographs of the sky using a camera which accurately followed the movement of the stars caused by the Earth's rotation. The asteroids move relative to the stars during the exposure and so, while the stars appear on the resulting photographs as points of light, the asteroids show up as tiny straight lines. By carefully searching the photographic plate with a magnifying glass (needed because the trails are often only a few millimetres long) new asteroids can be discovered comparatively quickly and their positions – as measured from the photographs – used to calculate their orbits. This method of new asteroid discovery has been used to the present day, both by dedicated asteroid searchers and by chance discoveries on photographs exposed for other purposes. Over 3000 asteroids now have well-defined orbits, and another hundred or so are added to the lists every year.

Most of the asteroids are very small. Only a few dozen are more than 100 kilometres in diameter, which makes them extremely faint when viewed from Earth. Only Vesta is ever bright enough to be glimpsed with the naked eye, and even then only under almost ideal conditions. This faintness – and the fact that they appear pointlike even when viewed through large telescopes –

makes the asteroids extremely difficult to study, and for many years they were largely ignored by astronomers. This antipathy was summarized by one well-respected astronomer who, exasperated by the number of asteroid trails on his photographs, referred to them as 'the vermin of the sky'.

Until the late 1960s almost all studies of the asteroids were concentrated on measuring their positions and, from these, determining their orbits with great precision. This established several important features about the asteroid belt – most notably that the asteroids were not, as Olbers and others had believed, the remains of an exploded planet, but objects left over from the formation of the solar system.

The asteroids are planetesimals which never managed to coalesce into a fully formed planet. We still do not understand the reason for this failure, but the gravitational field of nearby Jupiter was probably responsible. It seems that Jupiter accreted quickly and its gravity stirred up the planetesimals in the space between itself and the still-growing Mars. So a number of smaller objects of roughly equal size were formed, instead of one main body able to sweep up all the rest of the debris. Much of the material in the disturbed region was then either ejected from the solar system or captured by Jupiter, so that the total mass of the objects found in the asteroid belt today is small – inadequate to make even a tiny planet.

The orbital studies also showed that the asteroid belt was not just a collection of randomly orbiting objects – there was a very definite structure in the way their orbits were laid out. One important discovery was made by the American Daniel Kirkwood in 1857. Kirkwood showed that there were no asteroids with an orbital period equal to a simple fraction of the period of the planet Jupiter. He explained this by pointing out that the asteroids receive a small tug from the gravitational attraction of Jupiter every time they overtake the giant planet. For most asteroids these tugs occur at a different point around their orbit each time and have no lasting effect; however, if an asteroid were to orbit the Sun in a period that was a precise fraction of Jupiter's, it would receive these small tugs at the same point in its orbit time after time. The cumulative effect of these gravitational influences would be to change the orbit of the asteroid until the relationship between the asteroid's orbit and that of Jupiter was destroyed. Once the asteroid had moved out of the danger zone, the systematic effect of Jupiter on its orbit would vanish and the asteroid's orbit would stabilize. In recognition of this discovery, the zones of avoidance in the asteroid belt are now know as Kirkwood gaps.

The second discovery was made by the Japanese astronomer Hirayama Seiji, who noticed that the orbital characteristics of many of the asteroids were very similar; accordingly he grouped these asteroids into families. These Hirayama families are now believed to be the results of çollisions between two asteroids which broke up one or both objects and left a number of fragments in roughly the same orbit. The closeness of the family relationship provides a clue to how long ago the break-up happened: closely knit families are the results of a relatively recent collision, looser families are the debris from a very ancient event. The ages of the Hirayama families show that collisions within the asteroid belt are still occurring and that the original planetesimals, having failed to form a planet, are now in the process of grinding themselves back into dust.

The realization that the asteroids are probably examples of planetesimals – combined with the development of a range of new astronomical techniques – led to a resurgence of interest in asteroid science during the late 1960s and 1970s. Since the asteroids are far too small to have possessed either much internal energy or any trace of atmosphere, they could hardly have changed since they were formed in the early days of the solar system. This made them exciting objects for astronomers who, amazed by the photographs being returned by planetary probes, had regained their interest in the system and its violent history.

Studies at the wavelengths of both visible light and of infra-red – or heat – radiation were used to investigate the surface composition of the asteroids and to place them into a number of different compositional types. The most common types are S, for stony; C, for carbonaceous; and M, for metallic. There are several other classes including the U, or unclassifiable, types. There were attempts to relate these classes to various types of meteorites, but with only limited success. The distribution of the different types within the asteroid belt was also studied in an effort to derive some clues about the original solar nebula and it was discovered that, like the planets, the objects found nearest the Sun are predominantly stony. This new information is now being used to try and explain how the asteroids were formed and what prevented them from collecting together to form a planet.

Despite this intensive effort we know little about the asteroids, especially the structure of their surfaces and their bulk compositions. In particular, we know virtually nothing about the shape of most asteroids – although many are clearly irregular – or about the orientation of their axes of rotation. Much about these tiny worlds remains mysterious, but nothing more so than the fact that some of them seem to be able to escape from the main asteroid belt and move into radically different orbits.

It has been known for some time that a group of asteroids exist which share the orbit of Jupiter, but these are in orbits which are, due to a quirk of the law of gravity, stable. These 'Trojan' asteroids are probably planetesimals which evaded capture during Jupiter's formation. Far more remarkable is a group of asteroids which sweep in from the asteroid belt and cut across the orbits of the inner planets. These objects, small even by the standards of asteroids, are none the less extremely large in human terms and present a real and calculable hazard to the Earth.

The first suggestion that the asteroids were not confined to the asteroid belt came in 1873, when on 14 June James Watson, an American astronomer, discovered asteroid 132 Aethra. Although Aethra was kept under observation for only about three weeks, calculations of its orbit showed that at its closest to the Sun, it actually came inside the orbit of Mars. Sadly, after its initial discovery, the asteroid was not seen again for almost half a century – it was accidentally rediscovered in the 1920s. The existence of asteroids coming inside the orbit of Mars was, however, confirmed on 13 August 1898, when Gustav Witt discovered a small object which he named Eros. Not only did 433 Eros come inside the orbit of Mars but its mean distance from the Sun was less than that of Mars and its closest approach to the Sun was 1.3 AU, only about 22,000,000 kilometres outside the Earth's orbit. Eros held the record for the closest approach of an asteroid for over 30 years until, on 12 March 1932, the Belgian astronomer Eugene Delporte discovered 1221 Amor. The perihelion distance of Amor was 1.08 AU, allowing it to approach Earth within just 14,000,000 kilometres although its aphelion lay in the main asteroid belt.

Amor held its position as the closest approaching asteroid for just six weeks until, on 24 April, astronomer Karl Rienmuth from the Heidelberg Observatory in Germany captured an asteroid trail on a photograph. This trail looked interesting, so further photographs were taken and the object was observed for three weeks before its rapid daily motion across the sky caused it to vanish into the evening twilight. On 15 May 1932, the last time it was photographed for over 40 years, the asteroid was less than 12,000,000 kilometres from Earth.

Despite the short period of observation, there was enough information to calculate the approximate orbit of the new object, which showed that the asteroid actually crossed the Earth's orbit on its way towards a perihelion more than 50,000,000 kilometres inside the orbit of the Earth. These calculations also showed that if the asteroid had been just a little further ahead in its orbit in that spring of 1932 it would have missed Earth by less than 5,000,000 kilometres.

In view of the new asteroid's close approach to the Sun, Rienmuth decided to name it Apollo, after the Roman sun god, although the authorities decided that the orbit which had been calculated was too unreliable to accord the asteroid a permanent number. Instead Apollo was officially known as 1932HA, a code number indicating the year of discovery (1932), the fact that it was discovered in the second half of April (H) and that it was the first object found in that half month (A). Under this system the first object found in the first half of January gets the letters AA, the second object AB, until the middle of January is reached when the next discoveries are labelled BA, BB and so on until 1 February. Provided an astronomer remembers that the letters I and Z are not used, this code allows him or her to work out roughly when any asteroid with a temporary designation was first observed. These designations are used until an accurate orbit is calculated and the object has been reobserved on one more trip around the Sun.

Some astronomers spend many months trying to link sightings of two or more asteroids with temporary designations to prove that they are in fact different observations of the same object. If they achieve this, and the asteroid is assigned a permanent number, then the astronomer who calculates the orbit is often invited to name the new object.

It was obvious from its faintness that 1932HA Apollo was very small – probably less than 10 kilometres in diameter – and since its orbit was only poorly determined it seemed unlikely that it would ever be seen again. In fact, despite close approaches to the Earth in 1939 and 1941, it was not until 1973 that Apollo was rediscovered. Fortunately the 1973 observations were accurate enough to refine the calculated orbit and Apollo has now been given the Minor Planet Number 1862. Originally this unusual asteroid was considered to be something of an oddity, perhaps a single object which had somehow avoided crashing into one of the planets during its frequent trips around the Sun. The unique status of Apollo was not, however, to last for long.

On 12 February 1936 a second Earth-grazing asteroid was discovered and given the temporary number 1936CA. Orbital calculations showed that it had approached Earth to within two and a half million kilometres a few days before being discovered and that, like Apollo, its orbit stretched from well inside the Earth to out amongst the main asteroid belt. In view of this orbital similarity the new asteroid was named Adonis, after the mythological son of Apollo. Strictly this name was unofficial, since Adonis had been seen at only one apparition, but this detail had been set aside for Apollo, so it seemed appropriate to treat Adonis in a similar way. Like Apollo, Adonis was lost for more than 40 years before being accidentally rediscovered on St Valentine's day, 1977, from the Mount Palomar Observatory in California. Adonis has now been given the Minor Planet Number 2101.

The discovery of a second Earth-approaching asteroid within four years strongly suggested that there might well be other similar objects and, indeed, this proved to be the case. On 30 October 1937 an asteroid about 1 kilometre across missed the Earth by just 800,000 kilometres, passing by only twice as far away as the

Moon. It was given the designation 1937UB, named Hermes, and has never been seen again. Once again the observations made during the brief flypast were too few to allow its orbit to be calculated with certainty, and if Hermes is ever seen again it will only be by chance.

The close approach of Hermes drew increased attention to this new class of asteroids, but once again highlighted the difficulty of determining their orbits. All three of the Earth-grazing asteroids discovered in the 1930s (often referred to collectively as Apollo objects) were followed for only a few weeks before being lost again, preventing any subsequent observations. Only when the orbit of one such body could be determined with sufficient confidence for astronomers to predict its return would it be possible to plan detailed physical studies using large telescopes.

The discovery of each of these first three asteroids had occurred fortuitously, and it was some years before another Apollo asteroid was found. Designated 1947XC, the object was photographed twice from the Lowell Observatory in Arizona, but its orbit could not be well defined and it was lost again (it was eventually rediscovered in 1979 and named 2201 Oljato). Finally, in 1948, the jinx was broken with the discovery by Carl Wirtanen of 1948EA and 1948OA. Both these objects were subsequently relocated and they are now known as 1863 Antinous and 1685 Toro respectively. In 1949 Walter Baade discovered 1566 Icarus (1949MA), which was named after the mythological figure who flew too close to the Sun because its perihelion distance of only 0.19 AU (27,000,000 kilometres) takes it inside the orbit of Mercury. In 1951 A. Wilson and R. Minowski discovered 1620 Geographos (1951RA) during a sky survey project partly supported by the National Geographic Society.

After these successes the discovery of Apollo asteroids stopped for a while, although two other asteroids which almost, but not quite, crossed the Earth's orbit were found in 1950 and 1953. Now numbered 1580 Betulia and 1915 Quetzalcoatl, they are classified as Amor asteroids after the object with this type of orbit discovered in 1932. The distinction between the two groups is very fine, especially since Apollos can evolve into Amors and vice versa, so it is quite common to refer to Apollo-Amor objects. For convenience, the Earth-grazing Amors will be included with the Apollos here unless the difference is important in some way.

Despite the lack of new Apollo objects discovered in the late 1950s, the dozen or so already known raised a number of important questions for the astronomers of the day. The most obvious was simply: How many more of these Earth-grazing asteroids were still to be discovered? There were attempts to work this out by relating the amount of sky regularly photographed to the number of chance discoveries. From this sort of calculation it seemed that there could well be several dozen more Apollo objects yet to be found. This in turn raised the question: How could so many such objects exist? It was clear from the close approaches of Apollo and Hermes that collisions between the Earth and these asteroids could occur, and that while a collision was an extremely unlikely event during any particular encounter, a typical Apollo went around the Sun every two or three years – giving it plenty of opportunities for close approaches. Calculations showed that over the thousands of millions of years since the solar system formed it was almost certain that anything in Apollo-type orbit would eventually collide with one or other of the inner planets or be ejected into a different orbit during a close approach to a planet. It was just possible that one such object could have survived for so long, but the chance of Apollo, Adonis and Hermes all surviving was little short of miraculous. To make matters worse, these impossibly long odds got even longer every time a new Apollo object was discovered.

Of course, the astronomers of the late Fifties and early Sixties knew nothing about the cratering record on the other planets, and so were not to know that their estimates of the total Apollo population, based on the number of chance discoveries, was hopelessly wrong. It is now known that there are at least 50 times more Apollo asteroids than was believed 30 years ago, which makes the existence of so many objects even more difficult to explain. These revised population estimates have also dramatically increased calculations of the rate at which these objects strike the Earth, stimulating new research on the effect of an asteroid impact on the Earth's surface.

The new population estimates are based on two more or less independent sources: the cratering record on the Moon and planets revealed by space missions, and the results of a number of systematic searches for Earth-approaching asteroids started in the 1970s. Following the chance discovery of Apollo asteroid 1864 Daedalus by Tom Gehrels in 1971, a special search programme was set up in 1973 by Drs Eugene Shoemaker and Elanor 'Glo' Helin of the California Institute of Technology; this programme continues today. Using a telescopic camera with a wide field of view – known after its designer as a Schmidt camera – Shoemaker and Helin take as many photographs of a suitable area of sky as they can each month and then search the photographs for the trails of Earth-approaching asteroids. Each photograph is developed and examined within a few hours of being taken, so that if a candidate object is discovered further images can be taken on the following nights to allow the orbit to be calculated and other interested astronomers informed.

The effort involved in this project is enormous. During a typical observing run, which lasts four or five days, as many as 70 photographs may be taken. Each photograph is exposed for 10 to 20 minutes, during which the telescope must be carefully guided to compensate for the rotation of the Earth. As soon as each photograph has been taken the film is removed from the telescope and developed. The photograph is then immediately searched for asteroid trails by an astronomer who examines it millimetre by millimetre, using a binocular microscope. Every photograph taken during a night must be examined before starting the following night's observations. Only occasionally, perhaps once every few months, is a new object found and follow-up observations are made to allow its orbit to be calculated. The object then receives a temporary designation and its orbit is compared by computer with those of lost Apollo objects like Hermes. Sometimes bad weather may interfere and the chance for further observations of a suspected new asteroid may be lost although, under such circumstances, astronomers at another observatory can often be persuaded to help out by taking the necessary photographs.

Elanor Helin has continued this work for more than a decade and has discovered a number of new Apollo objects, including three with orbits which keep them inside the orbit of the Earth for much of the time. The first of these, 2062 Aten, orbits the Sun 20 times in 19 Earth years. The first five years of the programme led to the discovery of five new Earth-crossing asteroids, together with another seven which cross the orbit of Mars. To achieve this a staggering 80,000 square degrees of sky have been photographed, giving a discovery rate of less than one new object for every hundred photographs taken. It is a project which calls for considerable dedication and which, by the end of 1985, had discovered 22 Earth-approaching asteroids.

Elanor Helin is not the only person regularly searching for Apollo asteroids. Charles Kowal, best known for his discovery of asteroid 2060 Chiron which orbits between Saturn and Uranus, has found several, as have observers at the European Southern Observatory in Chile and at the Soviet Crimea Astrophysical Observatory. In addition, a search for fast-moving objects was carried out by John Davies and Simon Green using information returned by the Infrared Astronomical Satellite, IRAS, during 1983. As a result of these searches and occasional chance discoveries, there are now over 60 Earth-crossing asteroids known (see Appendix 1) and estimates of the total population of potential Earth-grazers place the number at about 1300.

The interest in the Apollo objects stimulated by this research has now led to the development of new, high-technology equipment to search for Apollo asteroids and comets. The latest of these is the Spacewatch camera, a project set up jointly by NASA, the Steward Observatory and the University of Arizona with additional funds from amateur groups interested in advancing space technology.

The Spacewatch camera uses a normal, computer-controlled telescope combined with an advanced electronic detector called a Charged Coupled Device, or CCD. A CCD is more sensitive than a photographic plate, so it can detect fainter objects, but its main advantage is that the electronic image formed on the CCD can be read directly into a computer. All that is necessary to discover moving objects with the Spacewatch camera is to take repeated images of the same region of the sky a few hours apart, and use a computer program to search for 'stars' which have moved between the two exposures. Since the information from the CCD detector is already stored electronically, all the computer is required to do is subtract one image from another, cancelling out the fixed stars, and report if there is any sign of an asteroid. If something is detected the computer, which already knows the positions of the asteroid and the times at which the images were taken, can immediately attempt to calculate its orbit and advise the waiting astronomers whether or not it is a new discovery.

Of course, in practice it is not that simple, since the computer programs required are very complex and must be able to distinguish between real moving objects and the false signals, or noise, which occur in all electronic detectors. The computer must also allow for apparent changes in the positions of the stars caused by fluctuations in the atmosphere which make the stars twinkle to the human eye. This development is now under way and the first measurements with the Spacewatch camera have already been made. Once the system is perfected, it may revolutionize studies of the Apollo asteroids and lead to many new discoveries.

Since many of these Earth-grazing objects could one day collide with our planet, it is important not just to know how many there are, but also to get some idea of their size. The Apollo asteroids must be small, because they are so faint even when close to the Earth, but exactly how small is rather more difficult to determine. The difficulty arises because, like normal asteroids, they never show any trace of a disc, making it impossible to measure their diameters directly. The only way we can estimate their size is to make a guess at the fraction of the sunlight falling on them which is reflected (their albedo) and, by combining their brightness as measured from the Earth with their distance, calculate the area facing the Earth. If the asteroid is spherical, we can calculate the diameter from the projected area.

Unfortunately, this technique has several drawbacks. For example, the albedo of the asteroids is not known and it is usual to assume some standard value, either based on the albedo of the Moon or on theoretical models of asteroid surface composition. Large errors can be introduced from this factor alone and the problem has bedevilled attempts to estimate the diameters of all the asteroids, not just the Apollos. New techniques based on simultaneously measuring both the amount of sunlight reflected by, and the amount of heat radiation emitted from, an asteroid have improved the accuracy of diameter determinations considerably. This method relies on the fact that all the sunlight which reaches the surface must eventually be either reflected as light or absorbed and then re-emitted as heat. By combining these two quantities we can calculate a value for the diameter which is much more reliable than that obtained by simply measuring the reflected sunlight and guessing the albedo.

A second difficulty in estimating the diameter of an asteroid is that whichever method is used, we must assume that the asteroid is spherical. While this is reasonable enough for a large main-belt asteroid, it is certainly not true for many of the Apollos. Accurate measurements of the light reflected from Apollo objects show that in most cases the asteroid gets brighter and then fainter over a period of a few hours. This is because most Apollo objects are irregular in shape, and as an asteroid rotates it presents a changing surface area to the observer and its brightness varies in a regular cycle. Of course the effect could be caused by the rotation of a spherical object with large albedo differences from one hemisphere to another, but it is much more likely that small bodies like the Apollos are irregular than that so many of them have such strange albedo differences.

In the case of several Apollo objects the changes in brightness are quite large, so they must be highly irregular. Probably the most unusual is 1620 Geographos, which seems to be a cigar-shaped body about 4 kilometres long yet only about 1 kilometre in diameter. Some estimates of the shape of Geographos are even more extreme, placing the length to width ratio at 6 to 1. The somewhat larger Amor object 433 Eros is also believed to be irregular, latest estimates suggesting that it is about 39 kilometres long but only about 16 kilometres across.

Although the irregular shape of the Apollos makes their sizes difficult to calculate, it does make it relatively easy to determine their rotation rates. This is done by recording the time an Apollo takes to undergo a complete cycle of brightness changes. These measurements show that most Apollo objects rotate within a period of a few hours.

We can also study the surface nature of the Apollos using ground-based telescopes. One of the most popular techniques for investigating the surface composition of an asteroid is to measure the object's brightness when it is viewed through a series of filters. Each filter allows through light of only a certain colour, or to be more precise, of a specific range of wavelengths. We can then compare the colours derived for the asteroid with the colours obtained from observing various areas of known composition on the Moon, or with laboratory measurements of either terrestrial material or meteorites. Observations made through a series of very narrow filters at infra-red wavelengths sometimes make it possible to identify specific minerals and thus get a fairly good idea of the chemical makeup of the asteroid's surface.

These detailed studies have shown that there are many unusual objects amongst the Apollo asteroids, but we can summarize their most important physical characteristics in a fairly general way. Most of the Apollos are between 1 and 3 kilometres in diameter, although since almost all of them are irregular this figure must be treated with some caution. The largest examples known are 2212 Hephiastos – discovered in 1978 – which is about 9 kilometres in size, and 1866 Sisyphus, which is probably slightly larger but can cross the Earth's orbit only under exceptional circumstances (433 Eros is not included here, since at present it does not cross the Earth's orbit). The smallest known example is probably 2340 Hathor, which is believed to be about 200 metres in diameter and was discovered in 1976 when it approached the Earth to within 1.6 million kilometres. Smaller examples certainly exist, but detecting such tiny objects is extremely difficult except under exceptional conditions. Hathor is probably only twice the size of the object which exploded over Tunguska in 1908.

Most of the Apollos, like the main-belt asteroids, are made up of rocky material. Some are covered by a layer of dust similar to that found on the Moon, but many expose considerable areas of bare rock. Rotation rates are generally only a few hours. Attempts to link the composition of specific meteorites to individual Apollo asteroids have not been successful, but the orbits derived for the three meteorites for which orbital determination has been possible are of the Apollo type, suggesting some sort of connection and providing another clue to the origin of the Apollos.

The orbital characteristics of the Apollo asteroids are varied, from examples which only just skim the Earth's orbit to objects like Icarus and 3200 Phaethon (1983TB) which sweep inside Mercury and pass very close to the Sun. Most Apollos have their aphelion somewhere inside the main asteroid belt, although a few are known which never travel beyond the orbit of Mars. Some cross the main belt completely and reach almost as far as Jupiter. Detailed calculations of the Apollos' orbits reveal that all are unstable and gradually changing under the influence of the gravitational attraction of the other planets. This means that each one, as its orbit evolves, will have a finite and calculable probability of colliding with one or other of the inner planets.

The advent of modern high-speed computers capable of dealing with the complicated mathematics needed to follow the evolution of asteroid orbits over thousands, or even millions, of years has enabled astronomers to calculate that the average lifetime of a typical Apollo asteroid is about 10,000,000 years. It can suffer one of three ultimate fates: it collides with another asteroid during a trip through the main belt; it flies close to a planet and is gravitionally ejected into a totally different type of orbit; or it is involved in a catastrophic collision with one of the inner planets, probably Earth.

The fate of Apollos ejected into new orbits is of no concern to the Earth, since they will almost certainly never be seen again. The chance that, once ejected, such an object might return to an Earth-crossing orbit is infinitesimally small. Similarly, an Apollo involved in a collision with a main-belt asteroid will be permanently removed from its Earth-crossing orbit – either the collision will radically change the asteroid's orbit or, more likely, one or both objects will be completely shattered. Some of the small fragments resulting from such collisions may remain in Earth-crossing orbits, and this may be the source of the smaller meteorites which fell on Barwell and in the Sikhote-Alin mountains.

Astronomers can also estimate the rate at which Apollo objects collide with each of the planets. The calculations for individual Apollo objects are not very reliable, but when calculating the overall collision rate most of the errors cancel out and the final result is probably about right. Duncan Steel and W. Baggaley, from the University of Canterbury in New Zealand, have carried out such calculations. They find that the Apollo most likely to collide with the Earth is the as yet unnamed object 1982DB. This asteroid was discovered on the night of 27/28 February by Glo Helin and Eugene Shoemaker using the 1.2–metre Schmidt telescope on Mount Palomar. Ironically, it was not discovered on one of their regular asteroid-search photographs but on one taken of a comet called DuToit-2/Hartley. Glo Helin noticed the asteroid trail while making a routine scan of the photograph with a magnifying lens 'just in case', but unfortunately, because it was not one of the regular asteroid-patrol photographs, there was not enough information available to tell in which direction the asteroid was travelling. Helin calculated the asteroid's two prospective positions the following night, depending on whether it was moving in a prograde or retrograde direction, and prepared to take another set of photographs.

The next night the weather was appalling and for a time it looked as if no observing would be possible, but finally the situation improved long enough for a photograph to be taken. Helin guessed that the object would be moving prograde and took the picture accordingly. Then, before the other photograph could be taken, the weather got worse again and there was no further observing. Helin hurriedly developed the photographic plate, but she had been unlucky – the asteroid was moving in the opposite direction and there was no sign of it. Worse still, that cloudy night had been the last allocated for her programme and the next night a different astronomer was scheduled to use the telescope.

Fortunately, astronomers tend to help each other out when important observations are disrupted by the weather, and the necessary photographs were taken on the following nights. The new asteroid was successfully relocated on these and a preliminary orbit was calculated for it. By calculating the orbit backwards in time it was found that 1982DB had passed only 4.1 million kilometres from the Earth five weeks before its discovery, making it one of the closest flypasts for several years. Future close approaches can be expected in the years 2002 and 2020, when the miss distances will be about 4.5 million kilometres. The calculations also showed that 1982DB orbits very close to the ecliptic plane, making it a strong candidate for a future space mission to explore an Apollo asteroid. If the preliminary orbit calculated for 1982DB proves correct, less energy is required to send a spacecraft to this object than to any other Earth-crossing asteroid.

Steel and Baggaley calculate that there is a strong possibility that 1982DB will collide with the Earth within a few million years, although the probability that it will make a near miss and have its orbit drastically modified is even higher. In any event, since the orbit of 1982DB is not known precisely these figures should not be taken too literally. They do, however, indicate how frequent Apollo asteroid collisions must be over periods of many millions of years. If the present estimates of the number of Apollos is correct, we can derive an average impact rate for each of the inner planets during the last 100,000,000 years or so. These results are only approximate, but since they agree quite well with estimates based on the cratering rate derived for the Moon and planets they are probably reasonably correct.

TABLE 3.2: Collision rates for objects 1 kilometre or more in diameter

Mercury	1 per 10,000,000 years
Venus	30 per 10,000,000 years
Earth	60 per 10,000,000 years
Mars	5 per 10,000,000 years

For the Earth, the collision rate could also be expressed as about one major asteroid impact every 160,000 years. The collision rate for objects in the Tunguska class (i.e. objects with diameters of about 100 metres) is of course much larger since there are many more small objects than large ones. Collisions with small asteroids are correspondingly more frequent, probably one every 10,000 years or so.

The rate at which Apollo objects collide with the Earth shows beyond doubt that they cannot be planetesimals left over from the formation of the solar system. The average lifetime of an Apollo asteroid is less than one-fifth of one per cent of the age of the solar system; it is inconceivable that over 1000 such objects could have survived so long. Accordingly the population of Apollo asteroids must be ephemeral, with the number of objects in Earth-crossing orbits being topped up in some way to replace those removed by collisions and gravitational ejection.

The transient nature of the Apollo population raises the very important question of where the new Apollo objects are coming from. One possibility is that they are small main-belt asteroids which have somehow been moved into Earth-crossing orbits; this could be achieved in one of two ways. The most obvious is that during a collision between two normal main-belt asteroids – the sort of event which generates a Hirayama family – one or more Apollo-sized fragments might be thrown out of the main belt. Unfortunately the velocity change needed to move from a near-circular orbit in the main belt to an eccentric Apollo-type orbit is about 6 kilometres per second. The energy required to produce this acceleration is about a thousand times more than that required to disintegrate asteroid material completely, so it is very unlikely that many new Apollo objects can be produced in this way.

An alternative method of ejecting small asteroids from the main belt without destroying them is to supply the necessary acceleration more slowly. This can be done only by the gradual influence of gravitational forces, notably those of Jupiter and Mars. A small asteroid in an orbit which is only just stable – for example an object near one of the Kirkwood gaps – might undergo a minor collision and have its orbit changed just enough to move it into the gravitational danger zone. Under the influence of Jupiter's gravity its orbit would change, and during this process the asteroid could fall under the influence of Mars. Computer simulations have shown that under such circumstances it is possible for a main-belt asteroid to be moved into a Mars-crossing orbit – i.e. be converted into an Amor object like 433 Eros – and from there be moved into an Apollo orbit by further close encounters with Mars.

Apollos could also be produced when a large main-belt asteroid is struck by one of its neighbours. If the collision is violent enough, the large asteroid might be shattered and kilometre-sized fragments flung into new orbits inside a Kirkwood gap. From there they would evolve into Earth-crossing orbits. The details of this process are still being worked out, and because of this uncertainty some astronomers prefer a second possible source for the Apollo objects: that they are the burnt-out remains of comets.

Comets are the dirty snowballs left orbiting on the fringes of the solar nebula during the formation of the planets. Many travel so far from the Sun that they can fall under the gravitational influence of other stars and have their orbits modified. The comet may then be lost into interstellar space or, just possibly, diverted into a new orbit which brings it into the heart of the solar system. In this case, as the comet falls in towards the Sun, it will begin to warm up. Sometime after it crosses the orbit of Saturn (the precise distance is still unknown), the heat from the Sun will cause the frozen outer layers to sublime, the ice turning directly into vapour and releasing any dust embedded in it. Once released, this material surrounds the snowball, or nucleus, with a diffuse cloud called the coma. Under the influence of the solar wind and the pressure of sunlight, the coma is blown away from the nucleus to form the tail or tails which characterize comets. The comet then proceeds around the Sun before returning to deep space along an orbit which may taken many millions of years to complete. As it recedes from the Sun, the nucleus cools down again and the loss of material from the outer layers ceases, causing the comet to fade back into obscurity.

Occasionally a comet chances to pass near one of the giant planets and during this close approach its orbit may be modified, preventing an immediate return to interstellar space. If the comet then suffers further encounters it can be permanently trapped in the inner solar system, orbiting the Sun every few decades. Comets trapped like this, orbiting the Sun in less than 200 years, are called short-period comets. With its large gravitational field, Jupiter is dominant amongst the planets in capturing comets and a number of the short-period comets are members of what is called the Jupiter family, orbiting the Sun every six years or so. The comet with the shortest known period of all is Encke's comet, which circles the Sun every 3.3 years in an orbit very like that of an Apollo asteroid.

This orbital similarity between some short-period comets and Apollo asteroids inevitably raises the possibility that comets might evolve into asteroids. Short-period comets are less active than comets making their first appearance to the Sun (for example, Encke's comet never gets bright enough to see without binoculars), because each time a comet goes around the Sun it loses some of its volatile material. This means that the comet is less able to form a bright coma or a large tail and so remains unspectacular. After repeated passages close to the Sun a short-period comet might become so inactive that its nucleus would no longer be hidden by the gas and dust of a cometary coma and it might take on the starlike appearance of an Apollo asteroid.

The theory that comets might evolve into asteroids received a boost in 1983 with the discovery of asteroid 1983TB. This object, which goes closer to the Sun than any other known asteroid, follows an orbit almost identical to that of the Geminid meteors. Since the Geminid meteors are believed to be the remains of a short-period comet which had faded away completely, leaving just a stream of dust orbiting the Sun, the orbital link between 1983TB (now designated Minor Planet 3200 Phaethon) and the meteors seemed to suggest that the asteroid was in fact the burnt-out nucleus of the original comet. Further studies of Phaethon made in 1984 have not confirmed this, but the link between the asteroid and the meteors remains unexplained.

Despite the discovery of Phaethon there are several theoretical difficulties associated with trying to explain how a short-period comet could evolve into an Apollo object. These include subtle, but important, orbital differences between the two classes of object and the difficulty of forming rocky and metallic meteorites inside an icy comet nucleus. Despite these objections we cannot rule out the possibility that at least some Apollos are decayed cometary nuclei, and a fuller discussion of the debate can be found in some of the references listed in the Bibliography. From the viewpoint of cosmic impacts the origin of individual Apollos is of little concern, except that it may affect their physical properties and hence determine whether or not they survive atmospheric entry intact. It does, however, raise the possibility that active comets, as well as inert ones, might strike the Earth.

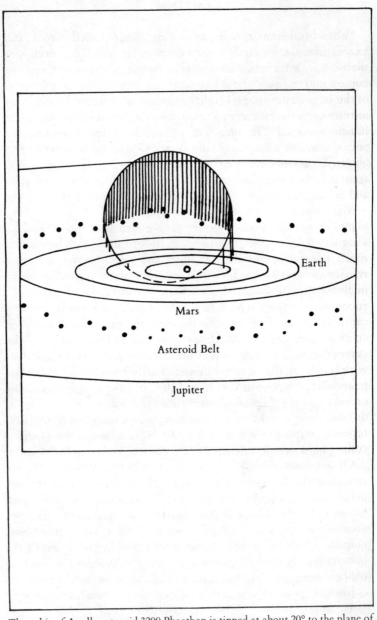

The orbit of Apollo asteroid 3200 Phaethon is tipped at about 20° to the plane of the solar system. At aphelion it is in the asteroid belt, but at perihelion it passes the Sun inside the orbit of Mercury.

When considering the probability of cometary impacts we must examine short- and long-period comets separately, because of their quite different types of orbit. We must also realize that the comets which are actually discovered are an insignificant fraction of the 10^{12} comets believed to exist in the Oort cloud, and a highly unrepresentative sample of those which enter the solar system. It has been calculated that there are between 500 and 800 short-period comets which cross the Earth's orbit, yet of these only about 20 are actually known. The true number of long-period comets is even less certain, since many must enter the solar system and escape again without ever being detected.

Most short-period comets are in orbits close to the ecliptic plane, because comets which approach the Sun in the ecliptic stand a higher chance of undergoing the encounters with Jupiter which result in their capture. Once captured, short-period comets tend to remain close to the ecliptic. Only a few are known with highly inclined orbits, and these are believed to result from close encounters with one of the giant planets sometime after they were captured. The fact that the short-period comets orbit in the ecliptic plane increases the likelihood of a collision when the comet crosses a planet's orbit. Comets in orbits highly inclined with respect to the ecliptic plane spend most of their time above or below the planets, and a collision can occur only if the comet crosses the plane of the planet's orbit at exactly the correct distance from the Sun. The short-period comets also make repeated trips around the Sun, increasing the likelihood that a collision will eventually occur.

Of course the lifetime of a short-period comet is quite brief; it is estimated that each comet will survive only a few thousand orbits before it is completely boiled away. Since a typical orbital period for such a comet is about 10 years, this gives a total lifetime of around 100,000 to 1,000,000 years after capture from the Oort cloud. Compared to Apollo asteroids, individual short-period comets have fewer opportunities to collide with a planet – because of their longer orbital period – and less time in which to have a collision, because of their shorter lifetime.

For an individual long-period comet – i.e. one which is making its first, and quite possibly last, visit to the Sun before returning to the Oort cloud – the probability of an impact is even less. This is because such a comet, even if it is in an Earth-crossing orbit, will have only two opportunities to encounter the Earth – once on the way in and once again on the way out. The probability of a collision is further reduced because, unlike the short-period comets, the long-period comets are not concentrated towards the ecliptic plane.

The orbits of the long-period comets are inclined at all angles to the ecliptic plane, because the orbits of comets in the Oort cloud are scrambled by the influence of passing stars. This means that the Oort cloud is a sphere, not a disc, around the Sun and long-period comets can approach from any direction. In many cases the orbits are inclined at such large angles that the orbit appears to have been tipped right over and the comet travels around the Sun in retrograde. Comets are the only members of the solar system to do this. Of course, these negative factors are balanced to some extent by the huge supply of long-period comets in the Oort cloud, but it is extremely difficult to calculate the rate at which these comets cross the Earth's orbit because of the almost random way they are discovered.

Attempts to estimate the rate at which active comets strike the Earth must try to allow for all these factors, and often use what are called Monte-Carlo methods. This technique, which is indeed named after the famous casino town, uses high-speed computers to simulate a population of imaginary comets with roughly the same general characteristics as the true one. A computer is then used to calculate the evolution of this population according to rules laid down before the simulation starts. These rules will include factors like the average lifetime of a comet before it evaporates away, the percentage of comets which break up spontaneously or are ejected following a close approach to a planet, etc. The computer then calculates the future history of the solar system over a period of millions of years to determine how many of these theoretical comets will collide with the Earth. The rules which govern the simulation can then be changed to try and find out which factors are important in determining the evolution of the comet population, and the rate at which active comets strike the Earth.

TABLE 3.3: Comets known to have approached the earth within 10,000,000 kilometres

Comet name or number	Date of flypast	Miss distance (km)	Geocentric velocity* (km/sec)	Notes
1491 II	20 February 1491	1,410,000	18.8	Orbit very uncertain
P/Lexell	1 July 1770	2,260,000	8.3	Never seen again
P/Temple-Tuttle	26 October 1366	3,430,000	21.3	
IRAS-Araki-Alcock	11 May 1983	4,680,000	28.2	
P/Halley	10 April 837	5,000,000	1.6	
P/Biela	9 December 1805	5,480,000	18.7	
1743 I	8 February 1743	5,830,000	14.1	Probably short-period comet
P/Pons-Winnecke	26 June 1927	5,890,000	26.9	
1014	24 February 1014	6,090,000	22.4	Unnamed
1702	20 April 1702	6,540,000	22.7	Unnamed
1132	7 October 1132	6,690,000	25.8	Unnamed
1351	29 November 1351	7,170,000	9.7	Unnamed
1345	31 July 1345	7,260,000	2.3	Unnamed
1499	17 August 1499	8,800,000	10.0	Unnamed
P/Schwassmann-Wachmann 3	31 May 1930	9,230,000	3.5	
Sugano-Saigusa-Fugikawa	12 June 1983	9,390,000	17.1	
1080	5 August 1080	9,590,000	19.6	Unnamed

* In the event of a collision the comet would be accelerated to a greater speed than this by the Earth's gravitational attraction.

P/ Denotes a short-period comet.

Other astronomers prefer to examine the number of real comets which have passed by the Earth and then estimate the biases introduced to the sample by various selection effects. One such attempt was made by Zdenek Sekanina and Don Yeomans of the Jet Propulsion Laboratory in Pasadena, California. They examined the catalogue of known comets and found fewer than 20 which had passed within 10,000,000 kilometres of the Earth and none which had come within 1,000,000 kilometres (Table 3.3). From this they attempted to derive an average impact rate of long- and short-period comets on the Earth over the last few million years. The closest miss distance known with any confidence was the passage of Lexell's comet, which missed our planet by about two and a quarter million kilometres on 1 July 1770. Despite this near miss, Lexell's comet is no longer a threat to the Earth, for in 1779 it had a close encounter with Jupiter and has never been seen again; presumably its orbit has been drastically modified.

Sekinina and Yeomans do point out that the comet of 1491 might have been closer to the Earth than Lexell's, but the orbit of this object is so uncertain that it is difficult to be sure exactly how close it did come. In our own century the record is held by comet IRAS-Araki-Alcock, which passed just 4.7 million kilometres from the Earth on 11 May 1983, making it one of the closest known of all time and certainly the closest since the 1770 passage of Lexell's comet.

The estimated rates of comet collisions with the Earth derived using this method is about one impact per 30–60 million years. Considering the large uncertainties, this is in broad agreement with the results of Monte-Carlo studies, although there is some dispute on the relative contribution from long- and short-period comets. Despite the fact that different astronomers give different values, most agree that collisions between the Earth and comets are less frequent than collisions with Apollo asteroids and it seems to be generally accepted that of the large objects which strike the Earth at the present time between 75 and 90 per cent are asteroids, the remainder being active comets. It should, however, be pointed out that this conclusion is based on the assumption that the number of comets entering the inner solar system has been constant over the last few hundred million years and this assumption has, as we shall see in Chapter 7, been challenged recently.

From this astronomical perspective we can now return to a terrestrial viewpoint, and search for evidence of catastrophic impacts on the Earth. From there we can investigate the physical and biological effects of such an event on the long-term evolution of our planet.

4

The Battered Earth

The surfaces of the planets and their moons reveal the violent history of the solar system, and our world cannot have escaped the collisions which battered its neighbours during the final stages of planet-building. The meteorite craters described in Chapter 1 are from small and comparatively recent events, but what were the effects of large impacts on the Earth many thousands of millions of years ago? Does any evidence of these ancient collisions remain?

Unlike the Moon, the Earth bears no record of its primitive crust. The surface of our planet is in a constant state of change caused by the action of wind and rain, and inexorable geological forces. Despite heroic searches by several generations of geologists, no terrestrial rocks more than about 3.8 thousand million years old have ever been traced and the nature of the Earth's original crust remains a subject of considerable speculation. In particular, the failure to discover any examples of very ancient terrestrial material has left geologists without many of the clues needed to resolve a major puzzle; what led to the division of the Earth's crust into the two fundamentally different types of material found today – the low-density continental crust and the high-density ocean floors? With the discovery of major impact features throughout the solar system, there is now a possible reason for this dichotomy. Impact craters may have been crucial in modifying the Earth's original surface.

The clue to this process can be found on the Moon. Like the Earth, the lunar crust is divided into two different types of terrain – the mountainous lunar highlands and the smooth, lava-filled maria. It was the effect of a cosmic bombardment on the original, low-density lunar crust which formed the mare basins and provided the opportunity for material from deeper in the Moon to pour out and fill them with lava. Could a similar process have operated on the primitive Earth?

From the evidence of other planets – as well as geological studies on Earth – it seems quite likely that our planet formed a low-density proto-crust as early as 4.4 thousand million years ago. This crust cooled and thickened during the next 500,000,000 years or so, and during this period vapours escaping from below the crust began to condense, forming the Earth's first oceans. From the record of impacts preserved on the other planets it is clear that while the Earth's proto-crust was evolving, more than 2000 craters with diameters greater than 100 kilometres would have been formed. Several of these were probably over 1000 kilometres across, comparable to the lunar mare basins. The total area covered by craters larger than 100 kilometres could have amounted to about 40 per cent of the Earth's surface, but since some of them must have overlapped, the actual area covered was probably only about 30 per cent. Many of these impacts would have penetrated the crust, causing severe fracturing of the subsurface rocks and perhaps promoting volcanic activity. Magma, rising up from below the crust via these volcanoes, would carry heat from the interior of the Earth to the surface, accelerating the cooling of the subsurface layers, but the most spectacular effects of this battering were yet to come.

The giant basins were formed on the Moon and planets about 3.9 thousand million years ago during a period referred to as the late heavy bombardment. At about the same time at least a dozen similar structures were probably formed on the Earth. The projectiles which formed the terrestrial basins were probably at least 30 kilometres in diameter and would have struck the Earth at speeds of about 20 kilometres per second. The impact of an object this size on the early Earth would be dramatic. The projectile would punch straight through the primitive crust and then release most of its energy as an enormous explosion which would excavate a cavity stretching deep into the mantle, the high-density rocky material found below the crust. This cavity would be unstable, and even while the crater was forming its shape would be changing as the walls collapsed inwards. The precise structure of the final crater depends on the nature of the material in which it was formed, but shortly after impact it would probably be between 10 and 20 kilometres deep and over 1000 kilometres across.

However, this would not have been the final form of the basin. The sudden removal of thousands of millions of tonnes of surface material would cause changes in the structure of the underlying rocks. The subsurface material, suddenly relieved of the load above it, would bend upwards in a process known as isostatic adjustment. This would raise the floor of the crater considerably, reducing its depth to only 3 or 4 kilometres and giving it the same sort of profile as the large lunar basins. The creation of these basins would have produced large areas several kilometres lower than the surrounding crust, but the ultimate effect on the Earth's evolution may have been more significant than mere changes in the local topography.

The sudden removal of large quantities of surface material has another important effect – it reduces the pressure in the rocks below the impact site. Since the temperature at which rock melts depends on its pressure, this reduction would allow subsurface rocks already near their melting points to liquefy. Depending on its composition, the liquid could be lighter than the surrounding solid (but highly fractured) rock and would rise to flood the floor of the crater in a very short time. This flooding would produce a terrestrial equivalent of a lunar mare. The lava which flooded the basin would contain a high proportion of material from below the crust and would therefore have a significantly different composition – and hence a different density – to the surrounding surface rocks.

The effects of the formation of terrestrial maria may have persisted long after the initial stages of basin formation and subsequent flooding with lava. The energy balance in the mantle below the basin would be upset and the local crust would be badly fractured, perhaps leading to an increase in volcanic activity. This would further modify the basin and its surroundings, since lava pouring out from these volcanoes would tend to flow into the low-lying basin, weighing down the floor and causing it to sink still further until a new isostatic balance was achieved. Water, draining to low-lying areas, would eventually flood the basin leading, at least superficially, to the basic division between continent and ocean.

This model for the evolution of the Earth's continental crust assumes that the original crust was of essentially low-density material. Some geologists dispute this, believing that the original crust – like the current ocean floors – was of comparatively high-density, basaltic composition. Paradoxically, the effect of large basin-forming impacts on such a crust would be much the same, except it may be the impact basins which form the continents, and the crust between which sinks to form the ocean floors. Which of the two suggestions is correct depends on the detailed nature of the original crust and, as we have seen, the failure of geologists to find any examples of very ancient material leaves this crucial question unresolved.

Since the details of this debate are beyond the scope of this book, we shall not pursue it further. The key point is that by the end of the last period of major basin-forming impacts, about half the Earth's original crust had been converted into low-lying – probably water-filled – basins while the other half resembled the cratered lunar highlands. More important than this superficial division into ocean and dry land was the development of two distinct types of crustal material, one significantly denser than the other; for this division is crucial to the process of continental drift, the major force for large-scale geological change on the Earth today.

The theory of continental drift has had a chequered history since it was proposed by the astronomer and geologist Alfred Wegener in 1912. Wegener's suggestion was that the low-density continental crust floated in the denser oceanic basalt, rather like a layer of sheet ice floating on water. He believed that a single piece of this crustal material, a supercontinent which he named Pangaea, had remained relatively intact throughout most of the Earth's history until it fragmented and the continent-sized pieces drifted apart. Wegener's theories were rejected by most scientists of the day, but evidence in favour of continental drift has been accumulating over the last few decades and the basic concept of slowly drifting land masses has now been generally accepted, although in a somewhat modified form.

The process which allows the continents to move is known as plate tectonics, and can occur because the crust is divided into a number of giant plates, probably in the region of 70 kilometres thick. The plates – there are probably six major ones – include both crustal material and the uppermost layers of the underlying mantle. Two of the major plates are wholly oceanic: the others consist of both oceanic and continental crust. The existence of different types of crustal material in the plates is essential for plate tectonics and – but for the evolution of the crust which began with the formation of terrestrial maria during the late heavy bombardment of the Earth – it would probably be impossible for continental drift to occur today.

The crustal plates lie above a layer of hotter and denser material which, although solid, is close to its melting point and can gently deform over long periods of time. This instability in the underlying material allows the plates to move relative to each other, although exactly how is not well understood. A number of processes occur at the boundaries between plates; the simplest is that the two plates slide slowly past each other. Unfortunately this is seldom very smooth and sudden jerks often lead to catastrophic earthquakes. Alternatively – for example at the mid-Atlantic ridge – new material from the mantle is rising to form fresh crust and push the existing plates apart. At other junctions new mountain ranges are being formed as one plate slides over the top of another, forcing the bottom plate back down into the mantle in what is known as subduction.

The process of sea-floor spreading followed by continental drift and subduction is extremely slow by human standards. America and Europe are drifting apart at only a few centimetres per year, but the gradual circulation of material has destroyed much of the Earth's very ancient crust. The oldest surviving areas of the Earth's surface are the Precambrian continental shields, which date back about 3000 million years.

Modern ideas about continental drift are still evolving and until quite recently it was thought that there may have originally been two large areas of very ancient rock which remained in place until about 200,000,000 years ago. These landmasses were known as Laurasia and Gondwanaland and were thought to have formed the nuclei around which our present continents developed. More recent thinking is that there may have been only one original supercontinent, but that it may have broken apart and then reformed two or three times in the last thousand million years. Whatever the precise details of the Earth's past, there is little doubt that the ancient landmasses eventually fractured and continental drift formed the pattern which we see on the Earth today.

It might seem that this gradual turnover of the Earth's crust should have removed any direct evidence for the really large impacts that occurred on Earth during the late heavy bombardment, but this is not necessarily so. It is possible that not merely the division into the continental and oceanic crust but the present shapes of some of the continents themselves may be due to the influence of very ancient collisions, whose more obvious features have long since vanished.

Collision with the Earth of an object a few tens of kilometres in diameter would liberate an energy of many millions of megatons. Such an explosion would, as has been described, form a crater hundreds of kilometres in diameter which might then develop into a terrestrial equivalent of a mare basin. The impact would also generate enormous shockwaves which would spread out in all directions from the impact site. The pressures in these shocks would be so great that the rocks through which they travelled would be welded together, forming a large and roughly circular . plug. As the shockwave spread out it would gradually weaken until it was no longer able to fuse the rocks together, but even when this point was reached there would still be sufficient energy to cause considerable damage to the structure of the crust around the edge of the fused region. At the edges of the plug a roughly concentric band of fractures would be formed as the remaining energy of the shockwave was dissipated. Could the formation of such a structure, described by the geologists who proposed it as an 'astron', affect the crust's subsequent development?

Despite its huge size, the original crater produced by a large impact would, geologically speaking, disappear very quickly because of isostatic adjustment, impact-induced vulcanism and erosion. No obvious trace of the crater walls would remain today. The overall shape of the circular basin would also disappear, because of the superposition of subsequent smaller craters – as seen

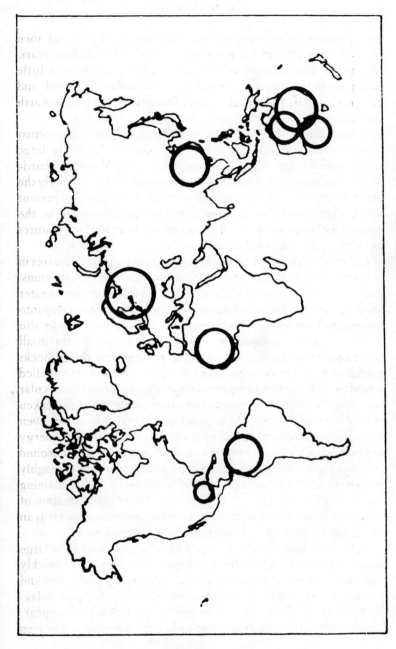

Possible sites for 'Astrons', giant impacts which may have shaped the continents.

on the Moon – or normal geological activity on the restless Earth. None the less, the existence of these huge and essentially circular plugs, with their surrounding zones of fractures, may have come to dominate the subsequent evolution of the continents. When the original land masses of Laurasia and Gondwanaland began to split apart it may be that the fractures, following the lines of least resistance through the crust, were guided by the underlying astrons.

The ancient crust may have cracked as a piece of glass will split, cleanly, along a line scratched into its surface. For example the bulge of Africa, which extends more than halfway around an almost perfect circle, may be the site of an ancient astron over 3000 kilometres in diameter, more than twice the size of the Imbrium basin on the Moon. Similarly, much of the eastern and central parts of Australia can be matched by three overlapping circles, two defining the bulk of the continent and a third cutting out the Great Australian Bight, whose curved outline runs along much of the southern coast. The almost circular Gulf of Mexico is also a possible site for an astron.

The idea that astrons sculpted the continents is highly speculative, and it will take much painstaking geological research to decide if it is true, but it does illustrate that the influence of astronomical events on terrestrial phenomena may be greater than we once imagined. This realization has certainly struck home on a smaller scale as searches for impact features on the Earth's surface have produced a rich harvest of terrestrial craters.

The search for impact craters on the Earth has been aided both by the advent of aerial photography and by the availability of high-quality photographs taken from Earth orbit. With the bird's-eye view provided by such images, we can detect faint circular patterns totally invisible from the ground. Such structures may be quite small – only a few kilometres or so in diameter – or extend for over a hundred kilometres. The term astrobleme, or star wound, has been coined for such a feature, and many have been discovered over the last three decades, although the mere fact that a structure appears circular is no guarantee that it is the site of a cosmic impact. Only when geologists have examined the area in detail can the extraterrestrial origin of a circular feature be confirmed or rejected.

It is important to realize that craters on Earth, especially extremely ancient examples, need not be the almost perfectly circular depressions which are found on the other planets. The final form of a terrestrial crater depends on the amount of material ejected and on the changes which occur after the crater is formed. Unlike most of the planets with large craters the Earth has an atmosphere, and air resistance reduces the distance ejecta can travel before falling back to the ground. The Earth's powerful gravitation attraction – six times that of the Moon – also limits the distance debris can be thrown by the initial explosion. For terrestrial craters the ejecta may be less than half the total volume of the material disrupted by the initial explosion. The appearance of the final crater also depends on how its rim is formed and what happens to the walls immediately after the crater is excavated.

Immediately after, or even during, the formation of a crater the walls will probably be unstable, especially if they are steep, and slumping will occur as they collapse inwards. The effect of this is to make the crater wider and shallower as the rim moves outwards and the floor is raised by infalling material. This early modification may continue for many years. Normal erosion and drainage may bring a considerable fraction of the ejecta back into the crater, reducing its depth and destroying its appearance still further. In very large craters there are also isostatic adjustments, as the underlying crust relaxes and flexes upwards because of the reduced load it has to bear.

These various modifications mean that shape alone is not enough to prove that a circular feature is of impact origin, especially since some of the characteristics of an impact crater can be mimicked by other geological processes. We need evidence that the rocks around the feature have been subjected to extreme changes of pressure and temperature. Such effects are called shock metamorphism, and they arise because at the moment of impact, temperatures of several thousand degrees and pressures of hundreds of atmospheres are generated in the target material. These conditions, which normally occur only several hundred kilometres below the crust, cause changes in the surrounding rocks which cannot be duplicated anywhere else on the Earth's surface. One

81

result is the production of unusual forms of common minerals, for example types of quartz known as coesite and stishovite. Another is physical alterations in the structure of the rocks, such as a change from a crystalline to a glassy state. Diamonds, produced by shock metamorphism of other forms of carbon, have even been discovered near impact craters.

On a larger scale there may be evidence for shatter cones, structures in which closely spaced fractures flare outwards and downwards from the apex of a cone. Often, many such cones are found close together and seem to point towards the centre of the original crater. An impact site may also be surrounded by material thrown out when the crater was formed. At the Ries crater, an impact structure in southern Germany 26 kilometres in diameter, a blanket of ejecta up to 100 metres thick surrounds what is now a roughly circular lake. Occasionally there may even be traces of the incoming object which formed the crater – the iron meteorites which lie in the Arizona desert around the Barringer Crater, for example – or more subtle but still detectable traces of extra-terrestrial material in the deposits surrounding the site.

To investigate the less obvious clues to the impact origin of an astrobleme, we need laboratory analysis of samples from in and around the crater. Thin sections of rock viewed with high magnification, often using polarized light for illumination, can reveal the presence of small droplets of melted material or other unusual microscopic structures. X-ray crystallography, in which X-rays passing through a tiny sample of material are diffracted by the atomic structure of the rock, may show that the regular arrangement of atoms within a crystal has been broken down. We can also find that argon gas, formed by the decay of naturally occurring radioactive potassium, has been driven off by the temperatures generated during the impact. Since the amount of natural argon present in rock samples can be used to date them, driving off the argon essentially resets the clock to zero. This can help to determine the approximate age of the crater.

Using these techniques, scientists have identified over 100 terrestrial-impact craters. Meteorite fragments have been found at only about a dozen of them, including the craters in Arizona and Siberia which were described in Chapter 1. In the others, identification is based on the presence of shock metamorphic effects in the surrounding rocks.

There is one other clue to an extraterrestrial origin for a suspected impact feature, although in some cases the evidence may be regarded as circumstantial. This is the association of the feature with tektites, small glass-like stones which are found in certain rather restricted areas of the world. The largest tektite field is probably the one which covers most of southern Australia, but there are also large fields throughout south-east Asia. Other smaller fields are located in Czechoslovakia, Africa and the USA.

Tektites are extremely unusual stones. They are made of silicate material and show clear evidence for having been molten. They are like small blobs of liquid rock which have solidified during flight through the atmosphere. Closer examination indicates that tektites have undergone two periods of heating. The first affected the entire object, while the second seems to have been restricted to the outermost layers.

Many origins for tektites have been suggested, including proposals that they are prehistoric attempts to make glass, sand fused together by lightning or fused rock left behind when nuclear-powered UFOs took off after visiting the Earth. These can be rejected after only a cursory study, but the tektites' true origin is still a subject of debate amongst geologists and astronomers. The two most enduring ideas are that they are material ejected from either the Moon or the Earth, which received its first heating in a volcano and its second during passage through the Earth's atmosphere.

Since known tektite fields are located in parts of the world where there is little or no vulcanism, the suggestion that tektites were ejected from lunar volcanoes was quite popular for a time. According to this idea, tektites were ejected from the Moon during particularly violent eruptions and cooled during the coast through space towards the Earth. They were then reheated by friction as they entered the atmosphere. The scarcity of tektite fields was explained by the fact that only a limited number of lunar eruptions would hurl material in the correct direction to reach the Earth. An alternative version of this theory suggested that the tektites were not ejected from volcanoes but were blasted out during the formation of lunar-impact craters.

Unfortunately for this scheme, the rocks returned from those parts of the Moon visited by astronauts bear no resemblance to any known tektites, virtually ruling out the lunar connection. Since terrestrial vulcanism also seems unlikely to account for the distribution of tektites, it is now believed that they are droplets of material ejected during crater formation on the Earth. This suggestion is supported by the fact that tektites are small, usually ranging in size from 1 to 10 centimetres, so could be thrown considerable distances, and that their wide variety of shapes are all consistent with being moulded by aerodynamic forces during cooling.

Thus the identification of a tektite field near a suspected crater provides circumstantial evidence of an impact origin, especially if the age of the crater and the tektites is similar. An example is the field of tektites in Czechoslovakia – known as the moldavites because they were found near the Moldau River – which is the same age as the 14.5-million-year-old Ries crater in nearby Germany. However, in some respects the crater–tektite connection is rather unreliable, since some scientists argue that because tektites are found near craters they must have been produced during impact, whilst others rely on the fact that tektites are found near individual craters to show that they are impact features.

Even discounting the evidence provided by tektites, the pace of discovery of terrestrial craters has been increasing steadily throughout this century. The impact origin of the Barringer Meteor Crater in Arizona was established around the turn of the century and the second confirmed crater, at Odessa in Texas, was identified in 1921. The Odessa crater is much smaller than the Barringer Crater, being only about 170 metres in diameter and a few metres deep. It does have a rim, but rises less than a metre above the ground. Excavations in 1939 revealed that the original floor of the crater was about 27 metres below ground level and that three smaller craters, now completely obliterated, had once existed nearby. The erosion of the outer rim to its present level, combined with filling over the years, clearly suggests that the Odessa crater is very old, a supposition confirmed by the discovery during the excavations of a fossil horse of a type now extinct.

Like the Arizona meteor, the object which formed the Odessa crater appears to have been metallic, since many iron meteorites have been found in its vicinity. The total amount of material recovered from the main and three subsidiary craters amounted to about 10 tonnes, more than half of this being recovered from the largest of the three satellite craters. From the sizes of the craters, and the distribution of the recovered meteorites, it seems that the original impacting body fragmented into four main pieces at low altitude. The largest of these exploded when it struck the ground, disintegrating and ejecting small fragments which fell in the crater walls and on the surrounding countryside. As in Arizona, no large fragments were found inside the main crater, supporting the conclusion that the largest Odessa fragment was destroyed by the explosion which formed the crater. The three other fragments had insufficient energy to explode on impact and simply buried themselves in the ground, causing mechanical damage, but no explosion. It is these fragments which make up the bulk of the material recovered from around the site.

A further decade passed before a third impact site was detected, 13 kilometres west-south-west of the Henbury Cattle Station in Australia, just a few hours' drive from Alice Springs. A group of 13 craters was discovered in May 1931 by A.R. Alderman, who was following up reports made to another meteorite researcher that iron fragments had been found in the Henbury area. Alderman was able to make only a brief survey of the site, during which he recorded a total of 13 craters and collected a number of meteorites, but subsequent expeditions explored the area more thoroughly. The most detailed research was carried out in 1963 by the US Geological Survey as part of a study of terrestrial impact craters made at the request of the American space agency, NASA, in support of the Apollo moon programme.

The 13 Henbury craters lie in an elliptical pattern covering a total area of about 1¼ square kilometres. The largest crater is highly elongated – 220 metres long, 110 metres wide and about 10–15 metres deep. This unusual shape is the result of two craters forming so close together that they had a common wall. Over the passage of time the wall has been eroded away, allowing the two craters to merge into one. Two other craters, 73 and 53 metres in diameter, lie very close to the main depression. The remaining craters are all less than 50 metres across and lie to the south and west of the main crater. This distribution reveals two facts about the impact which formed the crater field. Firstly, the incoming projectile must have fragmented at fairly low altitude, allowing all the meteorites to fall so close together. Secondly, since the heaviest fragments of a disintegrating meteorite are slowed less by atmospheric drag and thus travel farthest, the object must have been moving from south-west to north-east as it entered the lower atmosphere.

The Henbury craters are an unusual sight in the Australian desert because their shape makes them ideal for catching and retaining water. This has meant that they have acquired a rich covering of plants and trees, so that they stand out when viewed from a distance even though their rims are only a few metres above ground level. This effect is particularly noticeable in one crater – the second largest – which fills with water during the rains and contains trees which have grown to a considerable height. Some of these trees are estimated to be at least 300 years old, although the age of the craters is believed to be much greater.

The craters' age is uncertain, but they were probably formed within the last 5000 years. It is interesting that local legends recall that the craters were born in a fiery explosion. These legends may indicate that some of the early inhabitants of the region actually witnessed the formation of the craters.

The craters are now part of a conservation area managed by the Conservation Commission of the Northern Territories. Visitors to the site can follow a trail with signposts pointing out areas of interest and giving additional information about the craters and their formation. There is fragment of the meteorite, weighing 46.5 kilograms, in the museum at nearby Alice Springs.

Following the discovery of the Henbury craters, a number of other impact sites were identified in the 1930s including a group of seven craters at Kaalijarv, on the island of Saarema, Estonia, and the 175-metre-diameter Boxhole crater in Australia. Several more discoveries were made in the years after the Second World War, so that by the early 1950s the total had risen to 11 confirmed, plus about the same number suspected.

Towards the end of the 1950s a search was mounted for possible impact structures in Canada, using the results of an extensive programme of aerial photography. This was spectacularly successful and a number of new craters were identified, including the 200-million-year-old Manicouagan Lake in the province of Quebec. Manicouagan Lake is a doughnut-shaped body of water 70 kilometres across, with a broad circular peak of shocked rock rising from the centre. When viewed from above, especially from the vantage point of space, its resemblance to a large lunar crater with a central peak is remarkable.

Another feature recognized as the result of impact cratering was the two Clearwater Lakes further to the north of Quebec. The Clearwater Lakes consist of two circular bodies of water, about 20 and 30 kilometres in diameter, which almost overlap. The larger of the two, which lies to the west of the pair, has an almost circular ring of small islands within it; this circle of islands is concentric with the outline of the lake itself. At the centre of the lake lies a group of small islands which mark the top of a subdued central peak. The eastern lake, which is smaller, is deeper and although it too has a central uplift, this does not break the surface of the water. Like Manicouagan Lake, the Clearwater Lakes resemble lunar craters and are clearly of impact origin. Detailed investigation of the structure has confirmed that the present shorelines of the lakes mark the edge of the original crater rims, and geologists have traced disturbances in the underlying rock well beyond the rims themselves. The location of two craters so close together is of course not a coincidence, especially since they both appear to be about 290,000,000 years old. Presumably the impacting asteroid, which would have been a few kilometres in diameter, broke in two as it approached the Earth and the two fragments only had time to separate slightly before they reached the ground and exploded.

The discovery of these large and very ancient craters showed that astroblemes could be much bigger than the 1- or 2-kilometre structures identified before 1950, and that they might exert considerable influence on the local landscape. The success of the Canadian work encouraged other scientists to search for impact craters and, by 1972, 48 probable craters were listed. This list of

Craters on the Earth's surface. Open circles are craters with meteorites; closed circles are probable impact craters. Based on the data of Grieve and Robertson, see Appendix 2.

astroblemes has continued to grow – in 1979 the number of probable craters had increased to 78 and by 1982, when the Geological Society of America held a special meeting to discuss the possible effects of an asteroid impact on the Earth, the total had grown to 91 (see Appendix 2). The dozen or so craters associated with meteorites (Table 4.1) take the total number beyond the hundred mark, but they are not included in Appendix 2 because their meteoritic origin is beyond any possible doubt.

TABLE 4.1: Some craters at which meteorites have been found

Name	Location	Number of craters	Diameter of largest crater (metres)
Barringer Crater	Arizona, USA	1	1200
Boxhole	Northern Territory, Australia	1	175
Campo del Cielo	Argentina	20	90
Dalgaranga	Western Australia	1	21
Haviland	Kansas, USA	1	11
Henbury	Northern Territory, Australia	13	150
Kaalijarv	Estonian SSR, USSR	7	110
Moraska	Poland	7	100
Odessa	Texas, USA	4	168
Sikhote-Alin	Primorya Territory, USSR	122	26
Veevers	Western Australia	1	80
Wabar	Saudi Arabia	2	97
Wolf Creek	Western Australia	1	853

Not all these craters are as old as the Canadian examples described above. The 10-kilometre Lake Bosuntwi, the sacred lake of the Ashanti tribe of Ghana, was confirmed as an impact structure in the early 1960s by the discovery of coesite in the ejecta. This crater is believed to be just over 1,000,000 years old and is probably associated with the nearby Ivory Coast tektite field. A similar age is calculated for a 7-kilometre crater at Zhamanshin to the North of the Aral Sea in Kazakhstan, USSR. This crater also appears to be connected to a nearby tektite field. Another large crater, 19 kilometres in diameter, which contains Lake Elgygytgyn and is located near the Arctic coast of Eastern Siberia, is believed to date back about three and half million years.

These discoveries have allowed geologists to examine a number of terrestrial craters in great detail, and today impact craters are described as either simple or complex structures. Small impact craters form simple bowl-shaped depressions, about five times as wide as they are deep. Such craters – the Barringer Meteor Crater for example – often have a rim of raised, locally overturned rock. The crater is surrounded by ejecta, most of which lands within one crater diameter of the rim and shows inverted target stratigraphy, i.e. the material from the lowest levels of the crater lies on the top of the ejecta blanket.

When the crater diameter exceeds 2–3 kilometres – the precise size depends on the nature of the rock in which it is formed – it takes on a more complex shape. These complex craters are shallower, the diameter to depth ratio being about 10 to 1, and have broad, domelike uplifts, often in the form of a central peak or ring. Examples of such complex craters are Lake Manicouagan and the Clearwater Lakes in Canada. The material of these central uplifts may be severely shocked; this aids geologists in the task of identifying such features as impact structures.

It is not entirely clear how this central uplift forms, but the fact that it often contains layers of rock from below the level of the crater bottom indicates that there has been a definite upward movement of the underlying rock. Possible reasons for this include an elastic rebound of the crust, as it springs back into shape following the impact and overshoots slightly at the centre, or an isostatic adjustment of the underlying rocks to the sudden removal of millions of tonnes of material from the surface regions.

The variation in sizes and ages of craters of both types is of great interest because, in principle, it should allow the rate at which comets and asteroids strike the Earth to be calculated. Unfortunately, the true crater distribution is extremely difficult to establish since, although the age of an individual crater can be determined by detailed geological analysis, the number of craters on the Earth today reflects not only the rate of formation, but also the way in which craters are preserved once they are formed.

The two oldest impact structures so far discovered on the Earth are also the largest. They are the Sudbury basin in Ontario, Canada, and the Vredefort dome in South Africa. Both are about 140 kilometres across and date back almost 2000 million years. They were formed during what geologists and palaeontologists refer to as the Precambrian era, which represents the time when the first forms of life were emerging on the Earth. The Sudbury and Verdefort structures, although highly modified by erosion and subsequent geological activity, have survived so long because of their size and because they were formed in parts of the world which are geologically stable.

The impact origin of the Sudbury basin is well established because quantities of shock-metamorphosed rocks are preserved near its centre. The basin has been distorted by geological movements unrelated to its formation and has also been partly filled by large volumes of igneous rock, which flowed up from below the crust and then solidified. We do not yet fully understand whether this filling was triggered by the impact or by quite unrelated subsequent activity. The Sudbury basin is currently the source of much of the world's nickel; this productivity may be due to changes in the local rocks caused, at least in part, by the original impact. The Vredefort dome's similar origin, suggested by its central uplift and surrounding depression, has been confirmed by the presence and orientation of shatter cones and by the discovery of coesite and stishovite in the locality. With only one exception, these seem to be the only craters which date back to the Precambrian. All the other known terrestrial impact craters are less than about 600,000,000 years old, and most are much younger.

This preponderance of young craters (over a third are less than 100,000,000 years old) is hardly surprising considering the speed with which the scars of a cosmic impact are healed. Although small craters are formed more frequently than large ones, the lifetime of a terrestrial crater depends very much on its size. Large craters remain recognizable long after their smaller cousins have been destroyed by weathering, sedimentation and volcanic activity. On average, a crater more than about 20 kilometres in diameter will be recognizable for about 500,000,000 years; smaller ones will disappear more quickly.

Of course, the lifetime of individual craters may differ considerably from the average. A small crater may survive much longer than expected if it is preserved by special circumstances. An example of such longevity is a 14-kilometre-diameter crater in Northern Europe which dates back to the Precambrian era but was buried by sediments soon after it was formed and has only recently been uncovered. Similarly, the twin craters which make up the Clearwater Lakes in Canada are much better preserved than the Mistastin structure 500 kilometres away, despite the fact that all three craters are about the same size and the Clearwater Lakes are some 250,000,000 years older.

Another problem facing geologists trying to calculate the frequency of cosmic impacts is the distribution of craters across the Earth's surface. Of the hundred or so known astroblemes all are located on land, despite the fact that much of our planet is covered by oceans. This reflects not just the youth of the ocean floors (most are less than 180,000,000 years old), but also the extreme difficulty of examining the small-scale structure of the seabed in detail. The magnitude of these difficulties is highlighted by the fact that there should be several craters larger than 100 kilometres in diameter on the ocean floor, and not one has yet been found.

Several techniques have been put forward to locate oceanic craters, but since these are expected to be more subdued than examples on dry land, and sedimentation would smother, or even bury, a crater quite rapidly, simply searching for ringed structures on the sea floor using sonar or a similar technique is not sufficient. Other possibilities are to use data returned from satellites to try and detect gravitational anomalies, or to search for changes in the Earth's magnetic field caused when the crater disrupted the structure of the seabed rocks.

The distribution of craters discovered on the continents is also complicated by a variety of selection effects. Almost all the known craters are in the northern hemisphere and no fewer than 65 per

The Barringer Meteor Crater in Arizona, the result of a cosmic impact about 50,000 years ago.

The cratered far side of the Moon provides vital clues to the history of cratering in the solar system.

Apollo asteroid 2063 Bacchus moved relative to the stars during this 70-minute exposure and so appears as a streak of light.

Comet IRAS-Araki-Alcock came within 5,000,000 kilometres of the Earth in May 1983, the closest approach of a comet for nearly 200 years. During this 60-minute exposure the telescope followed the comet's motion, causing the star images to come out as trails.

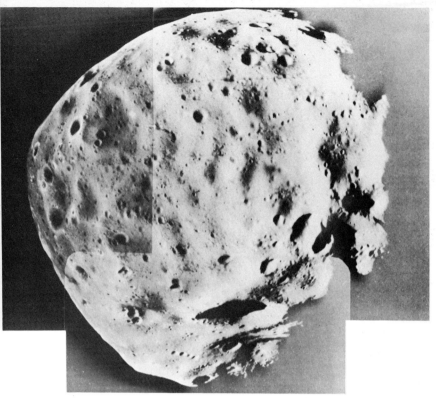

There are no detailed photographs of Apollo asteroids but they resemble Phobos, the innermost moon of Mars, pictured here in a mosaic of photographs.

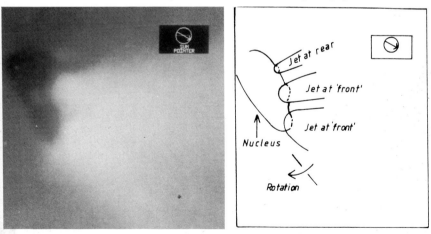

The nucleus of Halley's Comet, revealed by the Giotto spaceprobe, is dark and is ejecting material from a number of discrete jets. The nucleus is 10 kilometres across.

500 tons of buried TNT is exploded to form the Snowball crater. This test was one of a series of explosions in an experimental study of the cratering process.

The Dial Pack test crater, 50 metres in diameter, produced by exploding 500 tons of TNT.

A selection of Australian tektites, probably formed when molten rock thrown out of an impact crater solidified during flight through the air.

The Clearwater Lakes in Canada, site of an unusual double impact about 290,000,000 years ago.

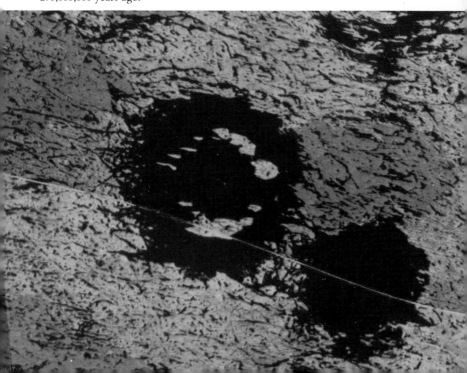

The Holleford crater in Canada, 2 kilometres across, is an ancient astrobleme, which has almost disappeared in the 500,000,000 years or more since its formation.

Wolf Creek, Australia is less than 1 kilometre across and is an example of a simple crater.

The 70-kilometre diameter of Manicouagan Lake in Canada is a complex crater with a pronounced central uplift. It is about 210 million years old.

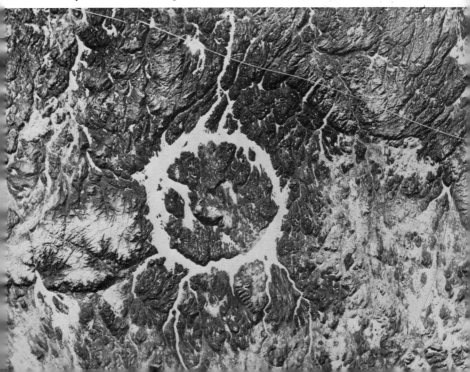

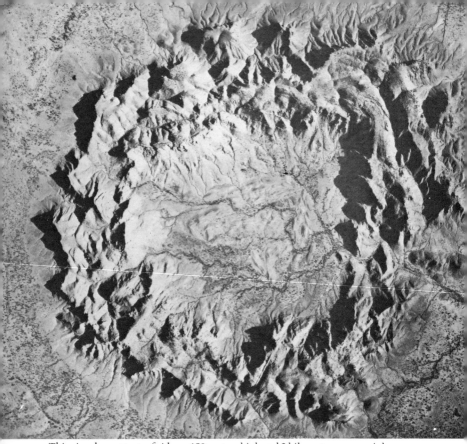

This circular pattern of ridges, 150 metres high and 2 kilometres across, is known as Gosse's Bluff in Australia. It lies at the centre of a flat, circular plain 22 kilometres across and is believed to be an impact feature, but its formation is not fully understood.

An unmanned spacecraft examines an asteroid at close quarters.

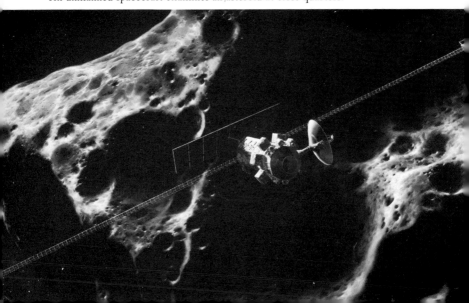

cent of them are on the North American and European continental shields, despite the fact that these together make up less than 11 per cent of the Earth's surface. The reasons for this imbalance are twofold. The continental shields are the oldest and most stable area of the crust and so preserve craters for long periods – but they are also the areas with the highest concentration of geologists interested in craters. The sudden increase in the number of craters found in the Soviet Union over the last few years (more than 20 between 1972 and 1978) reflects an upsurge in interest in crater studies amongst Soviet scientists. Since the Soviet Union covers such a large area, it is possible that more craters may soon come to light there.

Using the number of craters larger than 20 kilometres across – i.e. those which survive for long periods – on the stable North American and European shields, geologists have tried to calculate the cratering rate in these areas over the last 300,000,000 years or so. The estimates go back only about this far because much of the North American continental shield was covered by water about 450,000,000 years ago, and allowing for this makes the analysis more complicated. An age of about 300,000,000 years is also considered representative of much of the European area for which crater counts are available. The results for the two areas are then combined to try and improve accuracy. This combining is necessary because only 16 craters are involved and such small numbers can lead to large statistical uncertainties in the results.

Apart from the fact that they preserve craters rather better than some other parts of the globe there is nothing special about the North American and European regions, so the results from these areas can be used to estimate the cratering rate over the whole of the Earth's surface. The value derived from these calculations is somewhat uncertain, but it transpires that about every two million years there is an impact somewhere on the Earth large enough to produce a crater more than 20 kilometres across. Of course, the majority of these impacts will occur in the oceans, so the actual number of discoverable craters will be much smaller. Comparing this figure with the collision rates calculated by astronomers is quite difficult, because the precise relationship between the size of an impacting body and that of the crater it produces is not known.

This causes considerable uncertainties when trying to calculate the number of asteroids of any given size from the size of the craters, but none the less the figure calculated by geologists is quite close to the rate at which astronomers estimate Apollo asteroids and comets strike the Earth.

Since astronomers' estimates of collision rates depend on the total population of Apollo asteroids and comets, which is not known with any certainty, and those made by geologists depend on using the results from fewer than 20 craters spread across only 11 per cent of the Earth's surface, it is remarkable that these figures almost agree. In fact, the impact rate calculated by astronomers is slightly larger than the value determined by geologists, but in view of the large uncertainties involved most scientists agree that this difference is not significant. The agreement between the results of two completely different methods of investigating the same question is very encouraging and implies that most of the craters were probably formed by normal Earth-crossing asteroids. Since the general nature of these objects is understood, we can be fairly confident that we can calculate in some detail the effects of a cosmic impact.

5

Cosmic Impact

The fate of much of the cosmic debris which encounters the Earth is almost immediate destruction. This is because a collision between our planet and another astronomical object generally takes place at very high speed. The Earth travels around the Sun at over 14 kilometres per second, and this speed is fairly typical of objects in our part of the solar system. Even in the special case of material in an orbit which runs roughly parallel to the Earth's, and so either gradually catches up with our planet or is slowly overtaken by it, the Earth's own gravitational attraction will accelerate an incoming object to over 10 kilometres per second. Apollo asteroids, crossing the Earth's orbit almost at right angles on their way to or from the Sun, could impact at speeds of about 25 kilometres per second. Objects in cometary-type orbits can even meet the Earth almost head on – leading to much higher relative speeds, over 70 kilometres per second, at the moment of collision.

Dust grains, most no larger than the particles which make up cigarette smoke, orbit the Sun in uncounted numbers. Every day many millions of these are swept up by the Earth's gravity and enter the atmosphere. The very tiny examples, those smaller than about five microns (a micron is one millionth of a metre), are so small that they can be decelerated by the air without being totally vaporized; these eventually float down to the ground as micro-meteorites. Larger examples, perhaps up to a few centimetres across, are heated to incandescence by friction and flash across the sky in a brief, but spectacular, funeral pyre known to us from childhood as a shooting star. The luminous train across the sky, which may persist for several seconds, is more correctly termed a meteor and occurs at a height of about 100 kilometres. No trace of the original dust grain survives entry; it is completely burned away.

Meteors can occur sporadically or as part of a predictable

95

shower. Sporadic meteors arrive throughout the year and may appear from any direction in the sky at any time. On average six an hour can be seen from any dark observing site, but street lights and the light of the Moon often drown out the fainter ones. However, at certain times of the year, the number of visible meteors increases dramatically, and at such times most of them seem to be coming from roughly the same direction. This is called a meteor shower. Each shower is named after the constellation from which the meteors appear to radiate, although this is purely an effect of perspective. The meteors have no connection with the stars themselves.

TABLE 5.1: Some well-known meteor showers and their parent objects

Shower	Approximate date of shower	Typical number of meteors per hour	Parent comet
eta Aquarids	May 2–7	18	Halley
Perseids	July 27–Aug. 16	65	Swift-Tuttle
Orionids	Oct. 17–21	25	Halley
Taurids	Oct. 25–Nov. 25	10	Encke
Leonids	Nov. 16–19	15	Tempel-I
Geminids	Dec. 7–15	55	Asteroid 3200

Showers occur because, as well as the dust spread randomly throughout the solar system, some material takes the form of narrow streams following well-defined orbits around the Sun. Whenever the Earth passes through a stream the result is a shower of meteors. Since the orbits of both the Earth and the meteoroid stream are virtually fixed in space, the shower occurs at the same time every year and the meteors always appear from the same direction. Meteor streams are probably formed by dust shed from short-period comets, and most of the major showers have now been identified with specific comets. A few streams and their parent comets are listed in Table 5.1. The sporadic meteors probably result from old streams which are now so spread out that they are no longer recognizable, and from dust generated by collisions in the asteroid belt, slowly spiralling in towards the Sun.

The dust in meteor showers is too fine to survive the heat of re-entry and no meteorites have ever been seen to fall as part of a shower. The stones which do fall from the sky, like those which rained down on Barwell in 1964, result from pieces of inter-planetary debris much larger than cometary dust.

Objects larger than about 15 centimetres in diameter have a chance of surviving the heating they undergo during their flight through the atmosphere. During entry the surface layers may reach several thousand degrees centigrade, but these layers are burned off, or ablated, so rapidly that little or no heat penetrates to the centre of the meteorite. The atoms burned away, and the atmospheric gases heated by the passage of the object, produce a luminous trail along the object's track. This trail, much more intense than that of ordinary meteors, is often called a fireball. Sometimes the trail shows sudden brightenings as the meteorite breaks into fragments during entry, each piece following a slightly different path towards the ground. In such cases the material which reaches the ground falls as a shower of meteorites.

During its entry the object, sometimes called a bolide, is slowed down by friction and eventually loses almost all its original speed. The height at which this occurs is known as the retardation point, and for a typical meteorite this is about 20 kilometres. The altitude of the retardation point depends on the meteorite's size and composition – lower in the atmosphere for larger objects. Once this point has been reached, the fireball vanishes and the meteorite falls to the ground under the influence of the Earth's gravity. This free fall takes between one and two minutes, depending on the height of the retardation point. During this last stage of its journey to Earth the meteorite cools and is not usually warm to the touch by the time it reaches the ground.

Depending on its shape, which determines how it is affected by atmospheric drag, the meteorite reaches the ground at a speed of about 300 kilometres per hour. Small meteorites usually end up lying on or just below the surface, while the larger pieces can bury themselves quite deep in the ground or excavate small craters like those formed at the site of the Sikhote-Alin fall in Siberia. Despite the fact that one of the Sikhote-Alin fragments weighed over a tonne and a half, and that there was extensive local damage around the individual craters, there were no explosions on impact. The damage was all caused by mechanical energy and large fragments of the meteorite remained after the fall. Strictly speaking, holes formed in this way are called impact pits, not craters, but this fine distinction need not concern us here.

Not all fireballs produce meteorite falls. Many just fade out – presumably because the meteor is completely ablated away – and others seem to terminate in a sudden surge of brightness known as a flare. A terminal flare is probably the result of the incoming object disintegrating completely, and almost instantaneously, in flight and occurs when the aerodynamic forces on the object exceed the strength of the meteorite material. There is no generally accepted theory on exactly what happens during the terminal flare of a fireball except that often no major fragment of the incoming object survives and most of the shattered mass is contained in microscopic particles.

The objects which end their flight in a very bright terminal flare are probably larger than those which produce normal meteorite falls, although since the ability to survive entry depends on strength as well as size, this may not always be so. Whatever their size – and this is often extremely difficult to calculate – the bright fireballs take us into the range of explosive phenomena, cosmic impacts in which almost all the original body is disintegrated at or near the surface of the Earth. This marks the transition from large meteorites to what might be regarded as small asteroids, objects like those responsible for the Tunguska explosion of 1908 and the formation of the Barringer Meteor Crater.

Incoming bolides can explode in flight, or when they reach the ground, because the ability of atmospheric friction to decelerate a meteorite depends on its total energy. This in turn depends on the object's size and velocity – large objects penetrate deeper into the air before they are brought to a stop. For very large meteorites the retardation point is so low that the object either travels deep into the atmosphere or strikes the ground before it has slowed down appreciably. The fate of such an object depends on its ability to resist aerodynamic forces during its flight.

As we saw in Chapter 1, the object responsible for the Tunguska event entered the atmosphere and penetrated to a height of a few kilometres before exploding and devastating the Siberian forest. The failure to find any meteorite fragments led the original investigators to conclude that the object had reached the ground and been blasted to microscopic fragments by the ensuing explosion. This idea was taken up and modified to suggest that the Tunguska object was the nucleus of a small comet. This explanation was accepted for many years, and some astronomers even went so far as to suggest that the Tunguska object could be linked to a specific parent, Encke's comet. The comet theory has, however, been called into question recently.

In particular, calculations based on the trajectory of the fireball through the atmosphere have shown that the Tunguska object could not have been a typical short-period comet. If it was a comet then it must have been one with an aphelion at least 10 AU from the Sun. A comet on such an orbit would have entered the atmosphere at a speed of about 30 kilometres per second and, since eyewitness accounts suggested that the fireball followed a trajectory almost parallel to the Earth's surface, we can calculate the maximum aerodynamic pressure on the object as it pushed its way through the air. This works out to be close to the maximum compressive strength of iron and it is most unlikely that a fragile cometary nucleus could survive such a load. This suggests that the Tunguska object was not a comet, but a small Apollo asteroid.

If the Tunguska object was an asteroid, then its behaviour is much more easily understood. Since an Apollo object would be in a different type of orbit, its entry velocity would be lower than for a long-period comet. It would probably strike the atmosphere at about 10–15 kilometres per second. At this speed it would experience a peak atmospheric load about 10 times less than that suffered by a long-period comet on the same trajectory, and its rocky composition would give it more chance of surviving. Even so, the forces on the object would be extremely large and it is quite possible that while a meteorite composed predominantly of iron could just survive them, the strength of a stony object might prove insufficient. If this was the case, then the fate of the Tunguska object would be similar to that of numerous fireballs. After surviving most of the entry forces, the aerodynamic loads finally exceeded the material strength of the object and a terminal flare resulted as the bolide disintegrated about six kilometres above the ground.

The terminal explosion, as well as devastating the ground in the vicinity of the blast, reduced the Tunguska bolide to finely divided dust. Some of this settled out near the site of the explosion, some was swept up into the atmosphere. Unfortunately, nobody really knows how the shockwaves from such an explosion propagate through the air, so we cannot calculate exactly how much dust was injected into the stratosphere. It is quite conceivable, however, that it was enough to cause the bright nights reported over parts of Eurasia in the days following the blast.

There is other evidence pointing to an asteroidal, rather than cometary, nature for the Tunguska object. The suggestion that the bright nights after the fall were the result of the Earth sweeping up a comet's tail have been rejected, since the amount of dust required is several hundred times too much to be explained that way. Further evidence comes from tiny metallic spheres discovered in the ice near the South Pole. These have proved to be identical with similar spheres found near the site of the Tunguska explosion, and are believed to be debris burned off the fireball during entry. The composition of the spheres suggests that the Tunguska object was stony, like an asteroid. Studies of the samples from the ice also suggest that the mass of the Tunguska object was less than about 7,000,000 tonnes.

From the estimated entry speed and mass of the Tunguska object the energy of the terminal blast can be calculated – about 12 megatons, in good agreement with estimates of the explosion energy based on the blast damage and seismic effects. Finally, combining the estimated mass of the object with the density expected for an asteroid of predominantly stony composition, the object's size can be found – between 100 and 200 metres in diameter. An asteroid this small would be extremely faint and could certainly approach the Earth without detection. Even with a telescope, the Tunguska object would have been bright enough to see for only a few days before the collision. Although there is a slight chance that it might have been picked up on astronomical photographs taken in late June 1908, the chances of ever finding such an image in the archives is extremely small.

The Tunguska event is so well known, and so many different theories have been put forward to explain it, that it is a shame no photograph of its approach towards the Earth has ever been found. In the absence of such evidence, which might distinguish between a comet and an asteroid once and for all, it is likely that its true nature will remain a mystery.

Although there is doubt about the cause of the Tunguska explosion, which happened within living memory, there is little about the formation process of an explosive impact crater, even though none has formed in historical times. This is because this process has been investigated extensively over the last few decades, and what happens during a major cosmic collision is now reasonably clear. Understanding has come about because scientists have tackled the problem of studying impact cratering from a number of different angles including laboratory experiments, computer simulations, controlled explosions using nuclear and conventional explosives, and geological investigation of real impact craters on the Earth's surface.

The first person to carry out experimental studies of impact cratering was probably Robert Hooke, who in 1667 published the results of his investigation into the formation of lunar craters. Hooke dropped bullets into pipeclay slurry and noted that the resulting craters were similar to those observed on the Moon, although he also found that similar results could be obtained by bubbles bursting when a mixture of alabaster and water was boiled. Similar experiements were carried out in the 1890s by the American geologist G.K. Gilbert, who dropped balls of clay into a clay slab and observed how the shape of the resulting crater depended on the speed of the impacting body. Ironically, as we saw in Chapter 1, Gilbert did not accept that the Barringer Crater was of meteoritic origin.

Today these direct investigations continue, but with a much wider variety of experimental techniques. The simplest example of a high-speed cratering experiment is probably one which uses ordinary rifle bullets as projectiles. A typical .22–calibre rifle fires a bullet weighing a few grams with a muzzle velocity of about 400 metres per second. Such a gun can easily be incorporated into an apparatus which fires a series of similar projectiles into a range of different surfaces under identical conditions. By varying the angle at which the bullet strikes the target, and by changing the structure of the target material – usually finely divided sand – a number of different experiments can be made.

Of course the velocity of a rifle bullet is much less than the speed at which a real cosmic impact occurs, and to simulate these conditions realistically requires much more sophisticated equipment. An example of such an experiment is the NASA Vertical Gun Range at the Ames Research Centre in California. This can fire projectiles towards a target at speeds of up to 7 kilometres per second and at angles ranging from horizontal to vertical.

The impact chamber is a cylinder 3 metres high and about 2.5 metres wide, with viewing ports at the top and around the sides. The experiment uses one of three types of gun to accelerate the test projectiles, usually about half a centimetre in diameter, to the required speed and to fire them at a target from a range of about three metres. The projectile's precise speed is measured by a series of light beams which are interrupted as the bullet flies through them, and high-speed cameras, capable of taking up to 5000 frames a second, record what happens when the projectile strikes the target. If necessary the air can be pumped from the test chamber so that experiments can be carried out in a vacuum. It is also possible to arrange that the target is falling vertically at the moment the projectile strikes. In this way the crater-forming process on worlds with low gravity can be investigated.

After each test the experimenters examine the shape of the crater which has been formed and measure how much material has been ejected and how far it travelled before falling back to the surface. To help them do this the target is sometimes constructed of layers, or even columns, of differently coloured sand in which the deformation of the subsurface layers caused by the crater can be seen and photographed for further study.

Craters produced by this type of experiment are of necessity quite small – usually only a few centimetres in diameter – but since the conditions under which they are formed are very accurately known, they are extremely useful in investigating what happens during high-speed impacts. Nevertheless, real impact craters are thousands of times larger than these simulated ones, and to extend these studies to more realistic scales scientists have moved out of the laboratory and into the field.

Since the Second World War there have been a number of large-scale tests to determine the cratering effects of nuclear and chemical explosions. It must be said that the prime purpose of these tests was not to assist geologists interested in astroblemes; none the less many of the results are of interest when trying to understand what happens during the formation of an impact crater. Fortunately, although there might seem to be a great deal of difference between a high-speed impact and the detonation of a buried explosive charge, it turns out that the crater-forming process in both cases is quite similar. This has been demonstrated by comparing the results of small-scale laboratory explosions with those of impact experiments in which the energy of the test projectile and the laboratory explosive charge were similar.

The nuclear cratering experiments of the 1950s and 1960s started with fairly small weapons, typically with an explosive power of about 1 kiloton, buried between one and 22 metres below the surface. Depending on the depth at which the weapon was exploded, these resulted in craters between 28 and 90 metres in diameter and from 6 to 27 metres deep. The military nature of the experiments led to the craters acquiring some rather unusual codenames, such as Jangle U and Teapot ESS, which are still used today in scientific papers. These early tests were extended with more powerful explosions including the Sedan crater (almost 400 metres across and formed by a 100–kiloton explosion buried 194 metres below the surface) in an attempt to determine a relationship between the energy of an explosion and the size of the resulting crater. These scaling laws, as they are called, can be determined for the small craters formed in laboratory experiments and then compared with the scaling laws for much larger explosions. It then becomes possible, at least in theory, to work out the energy required to form a crater of any size by measuring its depth and diameter. It seems that the diameter (D) of a crater formed by a explosion is related to the energy of the explosion (E) by the equation $E \propto D^{3.5}$, expressing E in megatons and D in kilometres.

In practice, working out these scaling laws is complicated by the different kinds of rock in which the tests were carried out and the range of depths at which the explosions occurred, but in general they are found to be fairly consistent. There have been similar test explosions in the Soviet Union and at a research establishment in Canada (using conventional explosives) and these also appear to produce similar results. Once we can calculate the energy required to form a crater of a given size, studies of terrestrial impact craters can be used to estimate the kinetic energy of the object which formed them. These results can be linked to the properties of known astronomical objects such as asteroids and comets.

These test explosions have also been used to provide data for computer simulations of what happens during the formation of an impact crater. In these models the target is divided mathematically into a number of separate elements, and the effects of shockwaves, etc. on each of these elements is calculated in small time steps from the moment of impact onwards. Such calculations are both complex and time-consuming, but as experience of the technique has increased, better and better computer models have been developed. These models have been compared with the characteristics of real impact structures, like the Barringer Crater, and the results are extremely encouraging. Despite the fact that the explosions which created the Earth's impact craters were many times that of the largest nuclear cratering experiment, scientists now have a fairly clear understanding of what happens when an asteroid-sized object strikes the Earth.

The formation of the Flynn Creek Crater in central Tennessee, for example, has been described by Dr D.J. Roddy of the US Geological Survey, who based his analysis on a combination of field investigations, computer simulations and comparisons with explosive cratering experiments. Geological investigation of the site shows that the crater was originally about 4 kilometres in diameter and 200 metres deep. It was formed about 360,000,000 years ago, in a low and hilly coastal plain near the now vanished Chattanooga Sea. The site was probably covered by water a few metres deep when the impact occurred, but this would have had little effect on the cratering process.

Flynn Creek is an example of a complex crater, with a fairly smooth floor surrounding a central peak. Despite its small size, its main features have been reasonably well preserved in the surrounding rocks. The crater has survived because soon after it was formed it was filled with marine sediments, probably from the Chattanooga Sea. These sediments protected the crater from destruction until a few tens of millions of years ago, when major earth movements exhumed it.

Using the scaling laws developed from the cratering experiments described above, we can estimate the total energy required to excavate a crater of this size. Allowing for the uncertainties involved in extending the scaling laws to a crater this large, the energy required works out to be at least 25 megatons. Since no other energy source is involved, this must represent the kinetic energy of the incoming projectile. Kinetic energy is the energy which an object possesses due to its mass (m) and velocity (v) and is given by the simple equation

$$KE = 1/2 mv^2$$

From this we can estimate the mass of the object responsible for the Flynn Creek Crater.

No information is available on the object's trajectory before the moment of impact, so it is necessary to make an educated guess at its velocity when it struck the Earth. In such cases it is reasonable to assume tht the colliding object was in a typical Apollo-type orbit, so its velocity would probably have been between 15 and 25 kilometres per second. Using these values for v in the equation for kinetic energy, the mass of the projectile works out at between 1.3 and 3.6 million tonnes, with the smallest value being for the bolide with the highest speed. Of course, the true value could lie anywhere within these limits – or even outside them if the estimated impact velocity is wildly wrong – but at least this calculation shows that the object must have had a mass of a million tonnes or so.

With this estimate of the mass we can work out the approximate size of the bolide, a calculation which depends on the density of the projectile material. If the object was similar to an iron meteorite then it would have had a density of about 5 grams per cubic centimetre and a diameter of slightly less than 100 metres. Since iron meteorites are the densest type known, this represents the smallest probable size for the Flynn Creek bolide. If the projectile was made of stony material (which has a density of about 3.3 grams per cubic centimetre) it would have been slightly larger, and if it was an icy comet nucleus – density about 1 gram per cubic centimetre – it would have been larger still, probably about 200 metres across. The precise size depends on the object's mass and density. Since neither of these is known very accurately, these estimates should be used only as a guide to the nature of the bolide. All we can say with confidence is that it was about midway in size between a typical meteorite a few centimetres across and an Apollo asteroid a few kilometres across, and was probably comparable to the objects responsible for the Tunguska explosion and the Barringer Meteor Crater.

No trace of the projectile has ever been found at Flynn Creek. This is hardly surprising in view of the object's size when compared with the amount of material excavated from the crater, and the age of the site. If the projectile was iron, then any fragments like those found around the Barringer Crater would probably have rusted away completely in the millions of years since the Flynn Creek Crater was formed. In fact there are theoretical reasons, based on comparisons of the crater shape with the shapes of explosion craters, for believing that the projectile was not an iron meteorite but was of stony composition. This would mean that the diameter of the bolide was a little over 100 metres.

Assuming that these estimates are correct, the approach and impact of the Flynn Creek bolide can be described with reasonable accuracy. The incoming object would not have been affected by the atmosphere until it was within about 100 kilometres of the Earth's surface. At this point it encountered the very thin upper atmosphere and started to sweep out a narrow channel through the air. The bolide was travelling at supersonic speed, so the air molecules in its path would have had no time to move out of the way, and a conical shockwave would have developed with its point just in front of the projectile. This shockwave, continuously altering its shape as it penetrated deeper into the atmosphere, would accompany the bolide all the way down to the surface, but its effects would begin to be felt long before the moment of impact. The pressure developed along the front face of the bolide would be considerable, increasing to several tonnes per square centimetre within a few seconds of atmospheric entry. The rear face of the object would not be subject to these loads and the sudden build-up of pressure differences across the bolide would have caused severe stresses in the object itself. These loads could have led to the object disintegrating in flight and causing a massive terminal flare, but the Flynn Creek bolide, unlike the Tunguska object, was strong enough to resist these pressures and to reach the ground intact.

Objects like the Flynn Creek bolide are too large to be stopped by atmospheric drag, and so penetrate to ground level in just a few seconds. With an entry speed of between 15 and 25 kilometres per second, a large incoming object spends only about 10 seconds in flight, the precise time depending on its velocity and angle of entry. A near-vertical entry path takes about seven seconds, but a long flat trajectory may take double that, subjecting the object to greater atmospheric loads. In the absence of more definite data, an entry angle of 45° can be assumed for the Flynn Creek object, but the entry angle chosen makes little difference to the final result. During these few seconds, friction between the object and the air raised the temperature of the outer layers to several thousand degrees, vaporizing and ablating some of them away and trying to decelerate the bolide. However, the kinetic energy of the projectile was so great, and the time available so short, that the object's speed was only slightly reduced – and only a few per cent of its total mass removed – before it struck the ground.

At the moment of impact a number of highly complicated processes were set in motion, beginning with the formation of shockwaves which travelled down into the target material and simultaneously upwards into the bolide. To try and understand the details of what happened during the impact we need detailed computer simulations, and the development and interpretation of these computer models is extremely complicated. The following description is of necessity simplified, but does represent a general guide to what happened at Flynn Creek.

The shockwaves formed on impact travelled through both the target and projectile material with great speed, probably at more

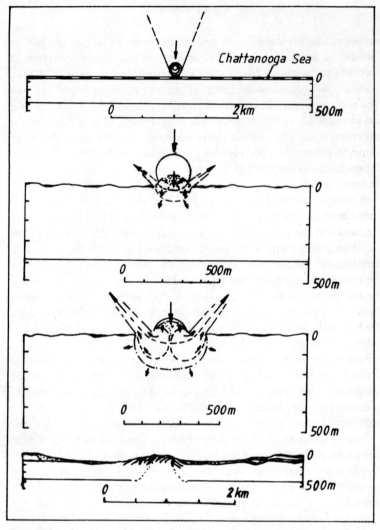

Formation of the Flynn Creek crater. Top: the bolide, accompanied by its supersonic shock wave, strikes the Chattanooga Sea. Upper middle: microseconds after impact, the lower portion of the bolide is being destroyed by expanding rarefractions and molten rock is being ejected from the edge of the forming crater. Lower middle: 0.1 seconds after impact the bolide is disintegrating and material is being ejected with considerable force. Molten rock still dominates the ejecta, but solid material will begin to burst from the surface in about another second. The central uplift will not form for several seconds after that. Bottom: final form of the crater, with a shallow floor and central uplift.

than 10 kilometres per second in both directions, but since the bolide was still travelling downwards even more quickly, all the projectile material continued on its downward course. As the shockwaves travelled through the rock they set up regions of very high temperatures and pressures at which the shock metamorphic effects typical of meteorite craters could occur. Within microseconds the pressures in the rocks surrounding the impact site had leapt to several thousand times atmospheric pressure and temperatures increased almost instantaneously to more than 1000°C. In less than a thousandth of a second these shockwaves had penetrated several hundred metres from the point of impact and the whole projectile was engulfed in a region of very high pressure.

The enormous pressures behind the expanding shockwaves had another effect. The strength of the projectile material and of the surrounding rocks would have been at least a thousand times less than the pressures involved, and these rocks were unable to remain solid. For a moment, part of the projectile and its immediate surroundings became liquefied and began to flow, initially lining the walls of the cavity and then, as the angle of ejection increased, jetting upwards and outwards from the point of impact. This material would have been ejected at very high speeds, perhaps as much as 80 kilometres per second, and would probably have been ablated away during its flight through the atmosphere. Under other circumstances, liquefied rock squirted out of a crater in this way could condense to form tektites.

Of course, the tremendous pressures set up at the moment of impact could not be sustained for more than a fraction of a second and as the shocked material relaxed, zones of reduced pressure, or rarefractions, were set up. These sudden relaxations normally travel behind shockwaves, where their effects are confined by the pressure of the surrounding rock, but when they approach the surface the pressure of the air just above the ground is totally inadequate to contain them. The rarefractions burst out of the ground and the sudden expansion of compressed material which follows hurls enormous amounts of material in all directions. Within a tenth of a second of the impact – and before the projectile had penetrated more than half its own diameter into the ground – rarefractions moving upwards through the bolide would have reached its rear edge and the sudden, and unconfined, expansion which followed would have destroyed the bolide completely.

Within another tenth of a second conditions had begun to stabilize, the shockwave had reached about one kilometre from the impact point and the ejection of liquefied rock from the centre had stopped. All around the point of impact huge pieces of rock were being hurled into the air as rarefactions broke through to the surface. This ejection of the underlying rock probably continued for up to another minute, throwing material several kilometres away and producing a broad, circular and essentially flat-floored crater. The ejection of material continued until the crater was about 130 metres deep and almost 3500 metres across.

During the formation of the crater – probably between five and 10 seconds after the impact – the ground 500 metres below the crater began to move, probably rebounding upwards after the passage of the shockwaves formed on impact. Blocks of rock a hundred metres or more across were lifted to the surface from almost half a kilometre below ground, shouldering aside what remained of the surface rocks to form a domed uplift, almost a kilometre across, at the centre of the crater. At the edge the slightly raised rim was formed quite late on, certainly in the second half of the crater-forming process.

The volume of the crater soon after its formation was about four-fifths of a cubic kilometre, with about 1000 million tonnes of material thrown beyond the rim. Most of this ejecta landed within about five kilometres of the impact point. Since the mass of the original projectile was only a few million tonnes at most, the bulk of this ejecta clearly came from the target material

In the years after the crater formed most of this ejecta blanket was removed, possibly by the action of waves from the nearby Chattanooga Sea which, although it flowed around the base of the crater, could not flow over its rim. Eventually the sea breached the walls, filling the crater, and over the next few million years the crater disappeared under the layer of black silty mud which subsequently preserved it for more than 200,000,000 years.

The region directly affected by the formation of the Flynn Creek crater – that is the area in which most of the ejecta fell – was less than 100 square kilometres, although blastwaves and other effects would have extended well beyond this. Survival in the immediate locality of the impact would have been impossible, but in global terms the area affected was insignificant. There would have been no lasting effects from that ancient explosion in Tennessee. This is fortunate, since there is a large number of objects with diameters of a few hundred metres in Earth-crossing orbits, and one probably strikes the Earth about every 25,000 years. The Flynn Creek Crater does, however, demonstrate the awesome destructive power of a cosmic impact. Observations of Apollo asteroids suggest that much larger objects can, and do, strike the Earth. What would happen if one did?

The largest known Apollo asteroid is about 10 kilometres in diameter, and considerable research has been done on the effects of a collision with such an object. This work has been stimulated by the suggestion that just such a impact, about 65,000,000 years ago, led to dramatic temporary changes in the Earth's climate and killed off much of the world's animal and plant life. The ecological consequences of such an impact will be considered later; for the moment only the physical effects will be explored.

The kinetic energy of a 10-kilometre asteroid, assuming it is in a normal Apollo-type orbit, is equivalent to about a 100,000,000 megatons. This is several thousand times the energy involved in the explosion of Krakatoa in 1883 and is roughly equivalent to exploding one of the warheads from a Polaris missile on every square kilometre of the world's surface, oceans included. Such a large amount of energy, especially when concentrated in a very small area, is so far beyond normal human experience that to predict its effects taxes our understanding of impact cratering to the limit. The use of scaling laws and computer models based on much smaller explosions is rather risky when dealing with such a large impact and may produce quite erroneous results, but these techniques will have to do until better ones are developed.

An impact on to dry land, or at least into a very shallow sea, has already been described, so we must now consider the impact of a large asteroid into the ocean. This is quite reasonable, since much of the Earth is covered by water, and that is where such an impact would probably occur.

111

Before the asteroid can strike the ocean, it must first penetrate the atmosphere. The diameter of a 10–kilometre asteroid is comparable to the thickness of the main part of the atmosphere, so aerodynamic drag would have virtually no chance of slowing one down during its entry. When the front face of the asteroid struck the ocean, the back edge would still be in the stratosphere, at about the height that jumbo jets fly.

A typical Apollo object would enter the atmosphere at about 15–25 kilometres per second and, at this speed, its flight through the air would last only a few seconds. Like the Flynn Creek bolide, the object would be travelling at supersonic speed and would develop a shockwave which would precede it towards the ground. Large aerodynamic loads would develop along the leading edge of the projectile, but it is not clear whether the asteroid would break up under the strain. Even if it did, the large pieces would all land very close together and the effect would probably be similar to that of a solid 10–kilometre body. A catastrophic terminal flare is unlikely; the asteroid is too large for this.

The bolide would drive straight through the atmosphere to the ground. Air pushed aside would not have enough time to flow in and fill this hole before the bolide struck the ocean, so the hole would still be open at the moment of impact. This is a major difference from what happens during the entry of smaller objects, and is extremely important in determining what happens in the impact's final stages. Otherwise, the entry of a 10–kilometre asteroid would probably be similar to that of the Flynn Creek projectile. As at Flynn Creek, very little of the object's total energy would be transferred to the atmosphere during entry, and only a tiny fraction of projectile material would be ablated during flight. The atmosphere, an effective shield against smaller particles, provides no defence against objects of this size.

After its passage through the air the bolide would strike the water and, compared with a 10-kilometre asteroid, the Earth's oceans are not particulary deep. The Marianas Trench, the deepest known point in the ocean, dips only about 11 kilometres below sea level and the average ocean depth is less than half this. This is not sufficient to stop a large asteroid travelling at around 20 kilometres per second, so the object would continue to drive down towards the seabed. The presence of the ocean would, none the less, play a key role in what happened next.

At the moment the asteroid struck the water, shockwaves would develop, travel outwards into the ocean and back upwards into the asteroid. Pressures immediately behind the shockwaves would rise almost instantly to several thousand times atmospheric pressure. The seawater would be compressed to several times its normal density and its temperature would rise to about 100,000°C. About a quarter of a second later the shockwave travelling downwards would strike the sea floor and, since ocean-floor basalt is denser than shock-compressed seawater, a second set of shockwaves would be set up at the seabed. One of these would travel downwards into the sea floor, while the other would bounce back up into the already compressed seawater.

Within half a second of impact, the shockwave travelling upwards through the asteroid would have reached its top edge and relaxation of the shocked material would begin, setting up zones of rarefraction. When the rarefraction developed, the highly compressed asteroid material would suddenly find itself free to expand and would do so very rapidly, destroying the projectile completely in the process. The sudden compression of the asteroid material and the surrounding water, followed by the very rapid expansion, would convert enormous amounts of energy into heat and this would be absorbed by the disintegrating asteroid and the ocean. Much of the asteroid material, with about the same volume of the water around the impact point, would be vaporized in the process.

This vapour, equivalent to several hundred cubic kilometres of water and rock, would explode out of the cavity forming in the seawater around the point of impact. The energy of this rock-and-water-vapour explosion would be equivalent to about 10,000,000 megatons and the vapour would be blasted out at several kilometres per second. Depending on whether the crater forming in the water around the explosion was strong enough to focus it, the cloud of vapour might be jetted upwards like a rocket exhaust, or just expand outwards more or less spherically.

About two seconds after the impact – at the same time the plume of water was being ejected – the shockwaves would have begun to work their way down into the sea floor. A shockwave would become roughly hemispherical as it penetrated the rock and, as it expanded, the inevitable rarefractions would develop in its wake reducing the pressures behind the shockwave and allowing the target material to expand. The sudden expansion would hurl rock and water radially outwards from the impact point to form a crater both in the sea floor and in the ocean. The shockwaves would continue outwards until they ran out of energy; the ejection of material would then stop. By then the crater would be about 60 kilometres across.

As soon as the ejection of material had ceased, the sea-floor crater would then begin to collapse, the walls falling in and the floor rising to form a central uplift. In principle the final crater would probably be almost 100 kilometres in diameter and about 500 metres deep, although the effects of water washing back into the cavity created in the ocean would dramatically alter its final shape. In particular, the sudden and violent return of the seawater would probably destroy the entire crater rim.

Despite the size and violence of its formation, the resulting crater is probably not the most important effect of the sudden arrival of a large asteroid. Tidal waves, with the effects of the blastwaves through the atmosphere, would affect millions of square kilometres around the impact site but unless the impact occurred close to the edge of the ocean, much of this energy would have been lost before it could affect the land. Even so, winds of many hundreds of kilometres an hour could be expected several thousand kilometres away from the impact site. These could blow for several hours.

The effect of tidal waves is rather more difficult to estimate, because the impacting asteroid is so much larger than the depth of the ocean. The normal methods used to calculate the development of large wave systems cannot be used under such circumstances, and the secondary effects of later waves formed by the collapse of the transient crater in the ocean complicate things. Experiments into water impacts carried out using the NASA Vertical Gun Range have suggested that the wave set up by the initial explosion might be as high as the ocean is deep, possibly as great as 5 kilometres, but such figures are little more than educated guesses.

It is also far from clear how stable such a huge wave would be, and whether it could survive long enough to reach the shore without falling apart or fading away due to internal effects, but what would happen should such a wave survive to reach the coast is not difficult to imagine. If the wave was still unbroken then massive and spectacular flooding of coastal regions would be inevitable, but it might well be that the effects of the shallower continental shelves would cause the wave to break long before it reached the shore, reducing its destructive power slightly. We need to do much more research into the properties of these waves before we can predict their effects with any confidence.

Surprisingly, the destruction wrought by the high winds and tidal waves following a large cosmic impact are probably not globally significant. Hundred-kilometre-an-hour winds are not uncommon during hurricanes, and their effects are fairly superficial. They blow over trees and houses, for example, but not mountains. Massive tidal waves have much greater destructive potential, but flooding would be confined to relatively low-lying areas and would not come inland to any great extent.

To put this into a planetary perspective, consider that everywhere within 1000 kilometres of the impact site would be totally destroyed – every tree flattened, all the fresh-water lakes contaminated by salt and silt, topsoil stripped away over huge areas and every living creature drowned. The total area affected would be a little over 3,000,000 square kilometres, but this huge area is only one-third of the size of Canada, and represents less than 1 per cent of the Earth's surface.

This shows that the material damage caused by the impact of a large Apollo asteroid is huge, but fairly localized. If there are any global consequences from such a collision then they cannot be from direct mechanical effects like blast, earth movements or tidal waves. Only the cloud of vapour and ejecta which is exploded out of the crater has any chance of affecting the entire planet, so the evolution of this material has been studied in some detail.

Immediately after the explosion the pressure of the vapour would be several thousand times that of the atmosphere around it. Such a huge pressure difference would allow the vapour to expand as if the surrounding air did not exist, shooting a cloud of steam and vaporized rock many kilometres into the air. In several respects this rapid expansion would be similar to a fireball formed by a large nuclear explosion, and results from nuclear tests have been used to try to understand what happens in the later stages of an asteroid impact.

An important factor is that the explosion would occur at roughly the same time that huge volumes of ejecta were being hurled out of the crater forming in the seabed. The ejecta would comprise both water and pieces of rock ranging in size from dust grains to giant fragments kilometres across. Pieces of ejecta larger than about a centimetre across would land quite near the crater, but the smaller particles would be swept upwards with the expanding fireball and lofted to great altitude.

It is difficult to estimate exactly what happens to these small particles. Once again the true situation is too complicated for existing computer models to calculate in detail, but it seems clear that many would be shot tens, or even hundreds, of kilometres into the air. Molten droplets of rock carried upwards, possibly all the way out of the atmosphere, would eventually solidify and, since they would be travelling too slowly to escape into space, fall back to Earth as tektites or microtektites.

As the cloud continued to expand upwards and outwards it would cool, and the vaporized rock would begin to condense to form small grains. A crucial question now emerges: How large are the particles of rock which condense out from the vapour? If they are larger than about 100 microns – that is a tenth of a millimetre – across (about the size of fine sand) then they cannot remain in the atmosphere for long and will fall to Earth in a few days. If the particles are smaller than about 10 microns, then the situation is rather different. Dust this small might remain in the atmosphere for much longer and, depending how much there was, could lead to severe climatic effects.

Once again this is controversial territory. Some scientists believe that the vapour will expand and cool quite slowly, giving the condensing grains time to grow quite large. Others believe that the condensation occurs rapidly and forms small grains which can stay in the stratosphere for months or even years. In practice, whatever the average size of a grain which condenses from the vapour, considerable amounts of dust would be created directly during the destruction of the bolide and by ablation from high-speed ejecta, so the production of at least some fine dust seems almost certain. Much of this dust would be lofted with the fireball into the stratosphere. The time taken for the dust to spread around the world, and its possible effects on the climate and the life below, will be discussed later.

As well as dust, the cloud of vapour raised by the impact would contain enormous quantities of water. Calculations show that the amount of water injected into the atmosphere by such a collision would be about 50 million million tonnes, although the precise figure depends on the composition of the bolide and the speed at which it strikes the ocean. To put this figure into context, it is about five times the amount of water vapour in the Earth's atmosphere under normal conditions. Strictly speaking, this figure is true only for an impact into an infinitely deep ocean – which is physically unrealistic – but it does at least provide an idea of the sort of quantities of water vapour involved. For a real impact into a real ocean this figure would probably be about 10 times smaller, but even so the amount of water vapour injected is comparable to the normal atmospheric water content.

The situation is, however, more complicated than just doubling the amount of water in the atmosphere. This is because water vapour is normally trapped below the tropopause, a layer of the atmosphere which begins at about 15 kilometres' altitude, but the vapour from an asteroid impact might well be pushed straight up into the stratosphere and beyond. The air at these higher levels is normally quite dry, and if most of the water vapour from an asteroid impact were to be transported to the stratosphere the effect would be to increase the stratospheric water vapour to thousands of times its normal level.

In principle, enough water vapour could be injected into the upper air to saturate the entire stratosphere, but in practice such a situation is not likely to arise. This is because all the water would have been evaporated from virtually the same spot, and in a very short time. The air within a few thousand kilometres of the impact site would be supersaturated with water vapour, but most of the rest of the atmosphere would be virtually unaffected. Since supersaturated air cannot hold all its water vapour for long, much of the water would condense out and fall as rain or snow long before it could be spread around the world by high-altitude winds. At a rough guess, most would have returned to the Earth's surface within a few weeks or months, so the sudden increase in atmospheric water vapour would probably not produce long-term climatic effects.

There is, however, a possibility that the sudden dumping of large quantities of water at these high altitudes might have other effects which are not immediately obvious. For example, the water vapour might upset the chemical balance of the upper atmosphere and deplete the ozone layer. Ozone is a special form of oxygen molecule – one which contains three oxygen atoms instead of the usual two – and at high altitudes a balance exists between the two different forms. Under normal conditions oxygen is converted to ozone at just the same rate that ozone changes back to normal oxygen, so the Earth's ozone layer, which filters out harmful ultraviolet radiation from the Sun, is maintained.

This fine balance would be upset by the sudden injection of even modest amounts of water vapour into the upper atmosphere where the ozone is found. The damage would be done because the water molecules would be broken up by the Sun's ultraviolet radiation to form other highly reactive species. These would speed up the conversion of ozone to ordinary oxygen, without speeding up the formation of more ozone. Worse still, these highly reactive species are not used up in the reaction which converts ozone to oxygen. After each conversion they are unchanged and can go on to destroy other ozone molecules.

The removal, or at least the depletion, of the ozone layer could have profound effects on the world below. For example, as it filters out the ultraviolet radiation from the Sun, ozone absorbs some energy and this helps to keep the upper atmosphere at its normal temperature. Removing the ozone layer would not only let more ultraviolet radiation through to the ground, but also cause a cooling of the upper air. This sudden cooling – together with the injection of vast quantities of water vapour – might, depending on just how far the temperatures in the upper atmosphere fell, lead to the formation of high-level clouds of ice particles. This would be helped by the presence of tiny dust grains from the impact which would act as centres around which the vapour could condense.

The effect of such a veil of clouds is problematical, since it depends on the size of the ice crystals making up the clouds. Under certain circumstances the ice grains can trap heat radiation trying to leak out into space and cause a global temperature rise; under others the clouds act to reflect away some of the sunlight falling on the Earth, producing a world-wide fall in temperature. It is even possible for the two effects to cancel out and produce no significant change at all.

There is yet another less obvious consequence of the entry and explosion of a large Apollo asteroid. The shockwaves generated during entry – and during the explosion soon after the impact – can produce chemical changes in the atmosphere. In particular they can cause nitrogen and oxygen, gases which make up 99 per cent of the atmosphere, to react together and form nitrous oxide, NO. The nitrous oxide would then combine with atmospheric oxygen to form nitric oxide, NO_2, some of which would go on to form nitrous and nitric acid by combining with water vapour. Over the next few weeks much of this material would be washed out of the atmosphere, forming massive amounts of acid rain.

As well as producing acid rain, gaseous nitrous oxide is harmful to both plants and animals once its atmospheric concentration reaches about 10 parts per million. An asteroid impact might produce enough NO_2 to cause severe damage to living organisms over a wide area, although dilution with normal air would probably mean that global concentrations would not exceed about one part per million. Other effects are possible. Nitrous and nitric oxides injected into the stratosphere could attack the ozone layer in much the same way as water vapour does, and with much the same effects. Finally, NO_2 is very efficient at absorbing blue light. Soaking up this much energy high in the air could affect the energy balance of the entire atmosphere, with major climatic consequences.

Recent research has focused on the effects of a large asteroid striking one of the oceans, but the existence of a few large craters like Manicouagan Lake shows that we cannot ignore the consequences of a land impact. It is interesting to consider how a large land impact might differ from an ocean impact. Perhaps surprisingly, computer modelling seems to suggest that in many respects the results of the two types of impact will be similar. This is because the fraction of energy lost as the projectile penetrates the ocean waters is small compared with its total kinetic energy, so the amount of energy delivered to the Earth's solid surface, whether seabed or dry land, is about the same. In both cases the crater would be formed in a similar way, although on land the crater rim would be better preserved because there would be no erosion caused by water flowing back after the explosion. Of course there would be differences in detail; for example much less water vapour would be produced in a land impact, so there would be little danger of saturating the stratosphere. The absence of an ocean would also mean that a larger proportion of the energy of the crater-forming explosion would be available to vaporize rocky target material, so there would be more dust. Apart from these sorts of differences it seems that the overall effects of land and ocean impacts – for example in terms of crater size and ejecta mass – would be about the same.

Since comets are also known to strike the Earth – albeit less frequently than Apollo asteroids – the effects of an impact by a cometary nucleus have also been examined by a number of scientists over the years. An average comet is believed to have a mass of about a million million tonnes and, impacting on to the Earth at about 45 kilometres per second (twice as fast as a typical Apollo asteroid), would strike the Earth with an energy of about 250,000,000 megatons. Calculations have shown that if all this energy went into heating the atmosphere the result would be a sudden rise in temperature of about 200°C, which would be fatal to most living creatures. By comparison, if totally absorbed by the much more massive oceans, the same energy would warm the waters of the world by less than a fifth of a degree.

These figures are of only academic interest, because in reality the energy liberated by the impact of a comet would be distributed between air, land and ocean in much the same way as would the energy of a large asteroid. Small icy projectiles – if such objects could survive long enough to collide with the Earth – might explode during atmospheric flight in a large terminal flare, but normal cometary nuclei are thought to be large enough to resist break-up and behave rather like a similarly sized Apollo asteroid. If this is correct, then the large-scale cratering effects of a comet impact are probably similar to those of an asteroid impact, although there may be some differences in the form of the final crater produced. It has been suggested that Gosse's Bluff – an unusual circular structure in Australia consisting of a ring of ridges about 150 metres high and 2 kilometres across in the centre of a circular, and almost flat, region 22 kilometres in diameter – may have resulted from a cometary, rather than asteroidal, impact.

A cometary impact may differ from an asteroid collision in one other important way. Asteroids are rocky objects, but the bulk of a cometary nucleus is composed of ices. It has been argued that the vaporization of these ices during an impact might lead to the release of many potentially harmful chemicals – for example hydrogen and methyl cyanide – with enormous quantities of carbon monoxide and carbon dioxide. Flooding the atmosphere or oceans with these chemicals might do serious damage to the environment and profoundly affect the entire Earth. However, it now seems that the temperatures reached during the early stages of a cosmic impact would be so high that individual molecules would be destroyed, stripped into their component atoms by the energy of the crater-forming explosion. The chemical consequences of a cometary impact may not be as significant as was once thought.

On balance it seems that the physical effects of impact by asteroids and comets, whether on to land or into the ocean, differ only in detail. They can probably all be described in the same way – disastrous.

6

Death of the Dinosaurs

The idea that the heavens influence events on the Earth is probably almost as old as mankind itself. Throughout history astronomical events, such as eclipses or the appearance of a bright comet, have been regarded as portents, usually of bad news. So universal was this belief that it has even found its way into our language. The word disaster derives from an expression meaning 'ill-starred'.

While few people today would flee from the sight of a comet, it is not difficult to imagine that in most early societies the appearance of a comet or an eclipse coincided with the death of a king, the failure of the crops, or some other kind of tragedy. In this way the connection between the heavens and the Earth became established and was formalized into the practice of astrology. Ancient astrologers sought to understand the movement of the Moon and planets so that they could give warning of eclipses, and in so doing laid many of the foundations of today's astronomy.

The concept of global catastrophe is also rooted deep in our subconscious. Many of the world's religions tell of a flood, or some other disaster, visited upon humanity in an attempt to wipe the slate and allow the flowering of a better world. Modern man, with his understanding of the solar system, can come to terms with the sudden appearance of a bright comet, but in view of our past it is not surprising that a link between comets and disaster has considerable emotional appeal.

The idea that comets might have an effect on the Earth is thus not new, and even after the development of the modern principles of scientific method many people have sought to link comets and catastrophe. The reader interested in this fascinating subject is invited to consult the Bibliography for further reading; these ideas will not be repeated here. We shall consider only modern thinking about the effects of a cosmic impact; with this in mind it is clear that collisions with Apollo objects, as well as with active comets, must play a crucial role in theories of evolution by catastrophe.

The evidence for catastrophic events throughout the Earth's history comes from the fossils which record the evolution of life on the Earth. Tiny fossils which resemble modern bacteria and blue-green algae, found in South Africa and Australia, indicate that the first primitive forms of life probably arose between about 3000 and 3500 million years ago, in the period known to geologists as the Precambrian. The blue-green algae of today are amongst the simplest forms of life known, single-celled organisms with no controlling nucleus. They are so simple that it is unclear whether they should be classed as plants, animals, or something in between. Such creatures are almost exactly what might be expected for the first forms of life to develop from the mixture of chemicals which probably existed on the early Earth.

From these first single-celled organisms more and more complex forms of life began to develop, and by Cambrian times, about 600,000,000 years ago, the seas contained many different species of plants and animals. Probably the best-known of these were the trilobites, creatures which had developed a central nervous system, multifaceted eyes, sensory antennae, a segmented body and multiple legs. The trilobites were very successful animals which in their heyday occupied almost all the available ecological niches in the oceans. Some swam free in the sea, others lived in shallow coastal waters and yet others scavenged in the sea-floor mud.

About 500,000,000 years ago – in a period known as the Ordovician – the first vertebrates (animals with backbones) appeared in the form of primitive jawless fish. About 150,000,000 years later life spread from the oceans to land, and soon after this the first reptiles appeared. The reptiles prospered, and from them developed the dinosaurs which, in one form or another, dominated the Earth for the next 100,000,000 years. The dinosaurs died out about 65,000,000 years ago and their place as the dominant terrestrial vertebrates was taken by mammals, warm-blooded creatures which went on to become the most important type of life on the Earth today.

From the way life developed from single-celled organisms to creatures like the trilobites and then on to larger animals such as dinosaurs, it might appear that this evolution was a smooth and gradual progression from simple forms to more complex ones. Closer examination of the fossil record, however, shows that this picture is far from the truth. It seems that instead of a gradually increasing number of species, after periods in which the diversity of life increased steadily there were times when enormous numbers of species died out almost simultaneously. After each of these mass extinctions the surviving species gradually diversified again, filling the ecological niches left vacant by the vanished creatures, before another mass extinction dramatically reduced their numbers. These extinctions did not simply affect small areas of the world, nor a single type of organism, but were wholesale and largely unexplained disappearances of apparently unrelated plants and animals on a worldwide basis.

The occurrence of these mass extinctions shows up clearly when the rate at which species became extinct is plotted against time. A very simple view of evolution would suggest that for every new species that evolved another would die out – in which case the rate of extinction would remain fairly constant throughout most of the Earth's history. Instead of this, the rate at which species became extinct shows enormous fluctuations, with long periods of stability punctuated by occasional mass extinctions. The rate of extinctions during the periods of stability is sometimes referred to as the background extinction rate, and it is against this that we must judge the severity of mass extinctions.

This process is not as simple as it sounds, for it assumes that the fossil record can be read unambiguously and that it is equally easy to read throughout the world. Regrettably, this is not the case. The traditional technique for dating fossils depends on the layer of rocks in which they are found, and for this to work the ages of the rock layers themselves must be estimated. The method of doing this is known as stratigraphy and relies on the fact that a vertical section through the Earth's crust reveals many different layers of rock, which may differ in composition, texture, colour or other physical ways. These characteristics reflect the conditions that prevailed when the rock layers – more properly known as strata – were formed. In principle the lowest strata should be the oldest, but in practice they are often found to have been overturned, or otherwise scrambled up, by subsequent geological activity. To add to the difficulties, individual strata may have been formed at different rates, since they are virtually all layers of sedimentary rocks formed by the solidification of sea-floor mud. If the rate at which material sinks to the sea floor changes, then so does the time needed to build up a layer of sediment with a certain thickness. Finally, although some stratigraphic boundaries are marked by obvious changes in the rock such as a thin layer of chalk or clay, not all are so clearly defined.

Because of these difficulties, the stratigraphic intervals into which the fossil record is divided are long and unequal, and the exact beginning and end points may be rather imprecise. This makes accurate timing of an extinction event – if it is judged by the sudden disappearance of fossils at a particular stratigraphic boundary – difficult to determine. To make matters worse, the rate at which new strata are created varies from place to place, so it is often difficult to relate the stratigraphic record of one part of the Earth's surface to another with any precision, compounding the difficulties in the search for simultaneous global extinctions.

Another complication arises from the fact that the transition from one stratigraphic layer to another is usually defined by the appearance, or disappearance, of a particular type of organism. For example this method, known as biostratigraphy, has been used to divide the Devonian era, a period beginning about 400,000,000 years ago and lasting for 60,000,000 years, into a number of parts. Two of these time intervals are known as the Frasnian and the Famennian periods. The Frasnian-Famennian boundary is defined by a sudden change in the nature of various marine organisms which appears to have occurred all over the world. In one stratigraphic level these organisms are commonplace, in the next they are nonexistent. We now recognize this sudden change as part of a global mass extinction; but it is the specific extinction of the marine creatures, not the mass extinction, that defines the boundary. We must be careful not to read too much into the apparent connection between extinctions and stratigraphic boundaries; extinctions are natural phenomena, but stratigraphic boundaries are artificial divisions created for the convenience of geologists and palaeontologists.

There is thus no precise definition of a mass extinction, either in terms of the percentage of species which die out or the time interval during which the extinctions take place, and inevitably different scientists use the term in different ways. In general though, a mass extinction could be defined as a period of a few million years or less during which several major groups of living creatures die out, or a large proportion of several such groups become extinct, or there is a substantial reduction in the diversity of life over a wide area of the planet.

Using this definition, a number of mass extinctions have been identified in the 600,000,000-year period during which multicelled life has existed on the Earth, sometimes called the Phanerozoic era. Because of the rather vague definition of a mass extinction there is some disagreement about exactly how many such events there have been, but up to 15 have been identified and more detailed examination of the fossil record will probably turn up several more. Of the known extinctions, five are generally regarded as being major events in which there were large global changes in the diversity of species. The others were less severe, affecting smaller numbers of species over a limited geographical area.

The most dramatic extinction of them all was the Late Permian event which occurred about 240,000,000 years ago. During this period more than half the animal families in the oceans vanished, including all the otherwise highly successful trilobites. The Late Permian extinction was a truly massive collapse of the world's ecology, although it seems that the decline was gradual, not catastrophic, and may have taken place over a period of several million years.

The four other major extinctions were less severe, but still seem to have been responsible for the removal of large numbers of animal families, reducing the total diversity of living organisms by perhaps a fifth in a comparatively short period of time. These events are usually referred to as the Terminal Ordovician (450,000,000 years ago), the already mentioned Frasnian-Famennian boundary, the Late Triassic (200,000,000 years ago) and the Late Cretaceous (65,000,000 years ago).

One of the first to consider these sudden extinctions was Georges Cuvier, who was born in 1769. Cuvier spent many years examining the fossil record and suggested that it should be possible to determine the relative ages of different groups of fossils. He was impressed by the mass extinctions he found, especially the profound changes which occurred at the boundary between the Cretaceous and Tertiary periods. Cuvier believed that the sudden changes in the fossil record were due to some periodic destruction and recreation of life, and he is today regarded as the father of biological catastrophism. He did not seek miraculous causes for the mass extinctions, but suggested that the task facing geologists was to find the reason for these changes by searching for evidence in the strata which contained the fossils.

Almost 200 years have passed since Cuvier set scientists this task, and despite the efforts of generations of geologists and palaeontologists there is still no general agreement on the causes of mass extinctions. In particular the reasons for the changes at the Cretaceous-Tertiary boundary, 65,000,000 years ago, have remained a topic for considerable speculation, not least because this period marks the end of the domination of the Earth by the dinosaurs. For this reason the subject of the Late Cretaceous extinction has considerable popular appeal. In fact the full extent of the extinction went far beyond the much-publicized destruction of the dinosaurs; its effects were even more severe in the oceans, with many types of microscopic plankton being totally destroyed and many larger types of marine animals disappearing.

We do not know with any certainty the precise period over which the Late Cretaceous extinctions took place; estimates range from a few years to a few tens of thousands of years. In geological and evolutionary terms, though, they happened very quickly. This has often led to the proposal that they were the result of some sort of catastrophe, rather than the end point of a gradual decline. In the case of the dinosaurs this suggestion is supported by two types of evidence from the fossil record. Firstly, there is no sign of a reduction in the number of species of dinosaurs in the period just before the mass extinction. Secondly, the geographical area they occupied does not seem to have been shrinking during the Late Cretaceous. It should, however, be said that like most aspects of

127

this puzzle, the view that the environment of the Late Cretaceous was fairly stable is controversial. A number of palaeontologists believe that many species – including the dinosaurs – were in decline towards the end of the Cretaceous period. If this is true, then the sudden extinctions 65,000,000 years ago might merely represent the result of a *coup de grâce* delivered to an already collapsing ecology.

The severity of the extinctions in the oceans compared with the land may be explained by the nature of the marine food chain. Plankton are one of the basic food sources in the oceans, and any sudden reduction in the amount of plankton would cause many of the larger marine animals to die out – either because they fed on plankton themselves, or because they fed on creatures that relied on plankton. In fresh-water lakes and rivers the extinctions were much less severe, presumably because many fresh-water creatures feed directly on plants or decayed animal matter and are not dependent on plankton.

There have been various attempts to explain the Late Cretaceous extinctions, and it is worth considering a few of the suggestions in a little detail. There seems little doubt that these extinctions were caused by some sudden stress on the environment, either from terrestrial or extraterrestrial causes, but the origin of this stress is still an area of active debate. It seems that there are almost as many theories as there are theoreticians, and no consensus has yet emerged on either the duration of the extinction or its cause.

Amongst possible internal causes, a widely held view is that the extinctions were caused by a dramatic reduction in the mean sea level towards the end of the Cretaceous period. A fall in sea level could well have induced climatic changes leading to the extinctions. If this explanation is correct, it implies that the duration of the extinction must have been reasonably long, since it would have taken some time for the sea level to change appreciably. Palaeontologists opposed to this explanation point out that some other dramatic sea-level changes have occurred in the past without being accompanied by mass extinctions, and that in any case the sea-level changes in the Late Cretaceous were comparatively small. None the less, the fact that plankton were amongst the creatures hit the hardest by whatever happened at the end of the Cretaceous does suggest that changes in the oceans may have been an important factor.

One possibility is that the salinity of the world's oceans was decreased for a short time, leading to the destruction of the ocean plankton. Studies have shown that a rapid freshening of the oceans could occur if there was a gradual build-up of fresh water in the Arctic Ocean, and this reservoir suddenly spilled over into the rest of the oceans. We know that fresh water flowing out of the River Amazon today can reduce the salinity of waters up to 2000 kilometres away, and the volume of water released by a sudden flood from the Arctic Ocean could be 2500 times greater than this and might have produced global effects on marine life.

Another possibility is a sudden change in temperature. Many species are quite sensitive to temperature changes, and a rise of even a few degrees in the average global temperatures could be lethal. Large reptiles, like dinosaurs, would be especially vulnerable to higher than normal temperatures. There is evidence for such changes during the Cretaceous period, but none of the variations found so far seems to be coincident with the terminal extinction event. The possibility of a brief but severe period of heating, or cooling, at the time of the extinction cannot be ruled out, but there is as yet no evidence for this.

A final possible terrestrial cause is an exceptionally severe period of volcanic activity. This could affect the environment in two main ways – either by injecting dust into the atmosphere and reducing the amount of sunlight falling on the Earth, or by dumping into the atmosphere quantities of poisonous gases. The main difficulty with this explanation is that periodic episodes of vulcanism are not uncommon in the Earth's history, and they do not seem to be correlated to mass extinctions.

With the apparent failure to find a totally convincing terrestrial cause for the extinctions, attention has obviously been concentrated on astronomical events. One proposal is that a surge in solar activity may have disrupted the Earth's ozone layer, suddenly increasing the amount of ultraviolet radiation falling on the Earth. Since excessive ultraviolet radiation is harmful to living creatures, this is a possibility; but the effect of a sudden burst of ultraviolet radiation on the world's ecology is poorly understood and much work needs to done to confirm this particular suggestion. There is no astronomical evidence, either, to suggest that our star is prone to sudden periods of increased activity, even though many other stars are.

Another quite popular theory is that the extinctions were caused by the explosion of a nearby star, an event known as a supernova. Supernovae are quite common. One occurs on average about every 50 years somewhere in our galaxy, and the last visible from the Earth was about 350 years ago. A supernova is the spectacular death of a large star, which ends its life in an explosion so powerful that for a few days it can outshine the light of all the other stars in our galaxy. With this in mind it is not difficult to imagine that the effect of a nearby supernova – for example one within about 50 light years (470 million million kilometres) – on the terrestrial environment could be quite serious.

The first result of a nearby supernova would have been the arrival of a powerful pulse of electromagnetic radiation lasting a few hours. This burst of energy would have disrupted the ozone layer and increased the amount of ultraviolet radiation reaching the Earth's surface. Depending how long the ozone layer took to recover, the increased levels of ultraviolet radiation might have been responsible for the destruction of much of the oceanic plankton, and indirectly many larger marine animals. A few years later (the precise time interval depends on how far away the supernova occurred) an intense flux of cosmic rays would have arrived. Cosmic rays are atomic nuclei travelling at close to the speed of light; they are harmful because they can disrupt vital chemicals within living cells. The flux of cosmic rays from the proposed supernova would have lasted about a decade and would certainly have affected much of the Earth's plant and animal life. Worst hit would have been the largest animals, while plants and trees would have been less vulnerable, possibly only suffering a slight reduction in their normal growth rate.

For a few centuries after the supernova, the Earth would be enveloped in the expanding cloud of gas blasted out by the explosion of the star. This would probably lead to slightly increased levels of background radiation lasting thousands of years. Although less severe than the enhanced flux of cosmic rays just after the blast, this radiation could be just as dangerous since it would be sustained for such a long period, producing cumulative effects on many generations of living creatures.

A supernova would seem to explain most of the features of the Late Cretaceous extinction except for one key point: there is as yet no evidence for a supernova anywhere near the solar system in the last 100,000,000 years. With this crucial flaw in the supernova theory, other astronomical explanations have been sought for the extinctions. Inevitably, many times, it has been suggested that a collision between the Earth and a comet or asteroid was responsible. The impact theory made a spectacular reappearance in 1980 when Luis Alvarez, a professor at the University of California, and his co-workers claimed to have found definite physical evidence of an asteroid impact precisely at the Cretaceous-Tertiary boundary.

The reason for Alvarez and his group's interest lies in the fact that certain metals are much less abundant in the Earth's crust than in typical meteorites. This is because these metals, notably those of the platinum group (i.e. platinum, rhodium, iridium and osmium) were concentrated towards the centre of the Earth during its early evolution and so are depleted in today's surface rocks. Low concentrations of these elements are, however, found in the sedimentary rocks built up by the slow deposition of material on the sea floor over long periods. These traces of the platinum metals in sedimentary rocks are believed to have come from extra-terrestrial material ablated off meteorites during their flight through the atmosphere, which subsequently drifted down to Earth and found its way into the mud on the ocean floors. Eventually this ocean-floor mud became incorporated into sedimentary rocks, preserving its extraterrestrial component.

Since there is no reason to believe that the average flux of meteorites on to the Earth has changed appreciably for many millions of years, we can use the iridium concentration in sedimentary rocks to estimate how long a particular layer of rock took to form. If large quantities of material were being laid down in the ocean over short periods, then the concentration of extraterrestrial iridium is low. On the other hand, if normal sedimentation has slowed dramatically, and the meteoritic material continues to arrive steadily, then the strata will contain a much higher-than-average concentration of iridium. Alvarez and his group set out in the hope of using the iridium concentration in a thin layer of clay which marks the boundary between the Cretaceous and Tertiary periods to determine the time it took for this clay layer to be laid down. This information would help to clarify how quickly the mass extinction at the Cretaceous-Tertiary boundary occurred, and perhaps rule out some of the possible explanations.

For their first measurements they choose a site in the Umbrian Apennines of northern Italy, where layers of sedimentary rocks laid down between 185 and 30 million years ago are exposed. Here the Cretaceous-Tertiary boundary is marked by a bed of clay about one centimetre thick, sandwiched between the uppermost layers of the Cretaceous and the lowest layers of the Tertiary rocks. Samples were taken from a number of different layers both above and below the Cretaceous-Tertiary boundary clay, and these were examined using neutron-activation analysis, which enables the relative concentrations of a large number of elements to be measured. A total of 28 different elements, mostly metals, were investigated in each of the samples, and the results were rather unexpected.

The relative concentrations of 27 of the 28 elements were fairly similar in all the samples analysed, with only small deviations from the average value. The surprising thing was that the concentration of the twenty-eighth element, iridium, increased about 30 times in the clay marking the Cretaceous-Tertiary boundary. Follow-up experiments were made to confirm this discovery and it was found that not only did the iridium concentration increase suddenly in the clay layer which marked the boundary, but the concentration fell again in the next few layers until it had returned to its original value.

Since nature can play some strange tricks, the first question to be resolved was whether there was some perfectly straightforward method which could build up excess iridium in the clay layer yet which would not concentrate any of the other elements studied. Measurements of other clay layers near the Cretaceous-Tertiary boundary showed no signs of an iridium enhancement, ruling out this possibility. The iridium seemed to be concentrated in the particular layer of clay which marked the Cretaceous-Tertiary boundary, and nowhere else.

The next test was to try and decide if this unusual iridium concentration was a phenomenon confined to this particular part of Italy. To do this Alvarez's group analysed samples of similar age from another part of the world. The spot chosen was Hojerup Church, near Copenhagen in Denmark. In this area the Cretaceous-Tertiary boundary is marked by a layer called the Fiskeler, or fish clay, which varies between a few centimetres to a few dozen centimetres thick, depending on its location. It is interesting that the Cretaceous-Tertiary boundary in both regions is marked by a layer of clay, although there are some differences between the two sites. For example, the fossils preserved in the Danish rocks show that they were laid down in shallower water than the equivalent layers in Italy.

Seven samples were taken from the Danish rocks near the Cretaceous-Tertiary boundary, and the concentration of iridium and another 47 elements was investigated. The results were similiar to those from the Italian samples – the clay which marked the boundary contained much more iridium than the layers above or below it. The excess concentration of iridium in the Danish rocks was even more pronounced than in the Italian samples. From these results Alvarez and his co-workers became convinced that the iridium excess in the boundary clay was a worldwide phenomenon. All that remained was to determine its cause, and to confirm that the excess did indeed occur all over the world.

The concentration of iridium in the boundary clays is about 60 times that in normal crustal rocks. If the excess iridium was due to material somehow concentrated from the crust, then measurable enhancements in some of the other elements should also have been seen. There was no evidence for this, suggesting that wherever the iridium in the boundary clay came from, it was not the Earth's crust. After ruling out the possibility that the enhancement came from a localized source with a higher-than-average iridium content – for example nickel sulphide or chromite ores – or that it was somehow extracted from seawater, it was a fairly obvious

133

step to suggest that the source was an influx of extraterrestrial material. Alvarez dismissed as too contrived the possibility that the effect was caused by a sudden reduction in sedimentation which allowed normal meteoritic iridium to build up over a long period, since it implied that a rather special set of conditions had affected both the Italian and Danish rocks at about the same time. He concluded that the extraterrestrial iridium must have arrived quite suddenly.

One possible source for this sudden influx of iridium was material blasted off a nearby supernova. To produce the required amount of iridium the supernova would need to have occurred quite close to the solar system, probably less than a light year away. This is much closer than any stars are found at present, and the probability of a supernova this close to the solar system within the last 100,000,000 years is about a thousand billion to one.

Despite its low likelihood, the possibility of a nearby supernova cannot be dismissed without considering other evidence. Alvarez and his group put forward two lines of argument against the possibility of a nearby supernova, both of which involved the formation of unusual isotopes during the supernova explosion. Isotopes are forms of an element which differ in atomic weight and in certain nuclear properties, but are identical chemically. Modern techniques can distinguish between different isotopes of the same element quite easily, and isotopic analysis is the key to Alvarez's rejection of the supernova hypothesis.

If a supernova was responsible for the excess iridium at the Cretaceous-Tertiary boundary, then the clay should also contain traces of other elements from the exploded star. Attempts to find these elements in the clay were unsuccessful. In particular, a certain isotope of plutonium, which would be expected if the source of the material was a supernova, could not be detected. A second clue lies in the ratio between two different isotopes of the iridium itself. Normal iridium exists in two forms and the ratio between these two isotopes is constant all over the Earth. Since the iridium was almost certainly present in the dust from which the planets were formed, we would expect the ratio of these two isotopes to be the same throughout the solar system. On the other hand, iridium produced in a supernova blast outside the solar system would probably have a quite different isotopic ratio from that of 'local' material. Comparison of the isotopic ratios of the iridium in the boundary clays with that in normal iridium deposits showed that the ratios are the same to within 2 per cent, strong evidence that the iridium in the clay did not come from outside our own solar system.

Since the results of the isotopic analysis suggested that the iridium was from inside the solar system – but its high concentration indicated that it was not from the Earth's crust – it was a fairly easy step to suggest that it was delivered to Earth by the impact of an asteroid or comet. To see if this proposal was reasonable in the light of what is known about potential Earth-colliding bodies, Alvarez and his colleagues set out to estimate the size of the impacting object. They did this by calculating the amount of iridium required to produce an anomaly similar to that observed in the Italian boundary clays spread over the whole of the Earth. Next they computed what fraction of the material blasted out during a large impact might be injected into the stratosphere and hence spread around the world in such a way that it could be incorporated into a worldwide layer. They based this figure on estimates of what happened during the explosion in 1883 of the volcano Krakatoa, which is believed to have blasted about 18 cubic kilometres of rock into the atmosphere, about one-fifth of which reached the stratosphere.

Assuming that a similar fraction of material would be injected into the stratosphere by an asteroid impact – and combining the total mass of iridium required with the abundance of iridium in typical meteoritic material – the mass of the impacting object worked out to be about 300,000 million tonnes. Assuming a density of 2.2 grams per cubic centimetre for the meteoritic material, this implied an object about 6½ kilometres in diameter. This is well within the range of sizes of the known Apollo asteroids, although it would be one of the larger and rarer members of the group.

A second attempt to calculate the size of the impacting object was made by assuming that all the boundary clay was composed of material that fell from the stratosphere following the impact. In this case the clay would be a mixture of asteroidal material and large quantities of terrestrial rock thrown up during the formation of the impact crater. Assuming that the ratio of asteroidal material to excavated crustal rocks was about 1:60 – and making the same assumptions as before about mass injected into the stratosphere and the density of the asteroid – Alvarez calculated the diameter of the impacting object to be about 7½ kilometres.

Since the conclusion that the iridium layer was caused by the impact of an Apollo asteroid seemed to be reasonable, the final step by Alvarez and his group was to see if the physical effects of an asteroid impact could produce the biological effects seen in the fossil record at the time of the Late Cretaceous mass extinction. As we saw earlier, the only way even a large asteroid impact can have global consequences is via the injection of material high into the stratosphere or beyond. Alvarez took the estimates of dust production from the Krakatoa blast and scaled them up to the magnitude of the explosion produced by the impact of an asteroid 6 or 7 kilometres across. This calculation suggested that sufficient dust would be thrown up to reduce the amount of sunlight reaching the Earth's surface considerably, perhaps enough to reduce the daytime light level to less than that of a full moon.

Light levels this low would be inadequate for photosynthesis, leading to a massive decline in the number of green plants. In the oceans, the photosynthetic plankton would soon begin to die out and much of the marine food chain would collapse. On land the destruction of the world's vegetation would starve plant-eating animals; this in turn would affect the carnivorous creatures which preyed on them. The destruction of the world's animal life would not have been total. Small creatures which fed on either insects or dead animal matter or vegetation might have been able to survive, and in the lakes and rivers decaying plant and animal material might have provided enough nutrients to maintain life for a while. Some of this decaying material might even have been carried into shallow coastal waters, where it could temporarily sustain some types of marine life.

Eventually the dust would settle out of the atmosphere and normal levels of sunlight would return. Surviving plants would begin to grow again; new vegetation would spring up from buried seeds and roots. The surviving land animals – mostly small mammals – would find that, with the larger creatures gone, the world would be theirs for the taking and would expand rapidly to dominate the land. The balance of nature would soon be restored, but the dinosaurs, and many of their contemporaries, would be gone for ever.

In many ways Alvarez's proposal seemed to fit several aspects of what happened at the Cretaceous-Tertiary boundary – for example the extinction of large land animals but not small ones, and the severe effects in the oceans compared with the land. The size of the hypothetical object was also reasonable compared with the sizes of known Apollo asteroids and the estimated diameters of typical cometary nuclei. With their apparent success in explaining the Late Cretaceous extinctions, Alvarez's group went on to note that the average period between mass extinctions was just over 100,000,000 years, and this interval was about the same as the interval between impacts of large asteroids. From this apparent coincidence they hinted that all the mass exinctions in the fossil record might have been caused by large impacts.

Alvarez and his colleagues recognized that, despite the success of the impact hypothesis in explaining the Late Cretaceous mass extinction, there were some important questions to clear up before it could be finally accepted. For example, it implies that all the extinctions occurred during the period of global darkness, estimated by Alvarez to last for a few years, yet many palaeontologists believe that they happened much more gradually than this. In particular, the extinctions of the oceanic plankton could have happened at a different time from those amongst land animals, and there is evidence that not all the various types of plankton died out at the same time. There are also reasons for believing that some dinosaurs survived beyond the boundary into the Tertiary period, although this is controversial.

Alvarez also recognized that no terrestrial crater of the appropriate size and age for a late Cretaceous impact has ever been found. His group did not consider this to be a serious flaw in the theory, because there is a two-thirds probability that the asteroid fell into the ocean, where a crater would be very difficult to locate. Even if a detailed search of the ocean floor were to prove unsuccessful, this would not be conclusive evidence that the theory was wrong; much of the ancient sea floor has been subducted during the last 65,000,000 years of continental drift, and the crater could have long since vanished.

On balance, it seemed to Alvarez and his group that the conclusions based on the iridium in the boundary clay were fairly secure, especially since they seemed to link the palaeontological evidence for a mass extinction with independent physical evidence for a sudden injection of material into the atmosphere. None the less, the impact hypothesis – or 'darkness at noon' as it was popularly described – raised a storm of controversy almost as soon as it was published.

A key aspect of this debate concerned the dust cloud presumed to have been injected into the atmosphere immediately after the impact, since this was ultimately responsible for turning a local disaster into a global catastrophe. A particularly important question was how much dust might be injected into the atmosphere, and how long it could remain suspended in the air before falling back to Earth. This would determine the duration and intensity of the subsequent global blackout, and thus the impact's long-term biological consequences.

Alvarez based his estimates of how much dust might be distributed throughout the atmosphere following an asteroid impact on observations of material ejected from the Krakatoa volcano. Large volcanic eruptions are relatively common, and are often followed by months or years of unusual twilights and spectacular sunsets caused by the eruption's injection of considerable quantities of material into the stratosphere. These effects have been studied for many years, and we understand fairly well the behaviour of volcanic debris in the atmosphere. Since volcanic eruptions are amongst the most energetic explosions which occur on the Earth's surface, they obviously provide a starting point when considering the effects of dust raised by an asteroid impact. We must, however, realize that there are differences, as well as similarities, between the the two types of event.

One of these differences – crucial when calculating the length of the blackout caused by an asteroid impact – is that most of the material remaining in the stratosphere after a volcanic eruption is not dust, but composed of tiny liquid droplets. These droplets are produced when sulphur dioxide gas, squirted high into the air during the eruption, combines with stratospheric water vapour to form sulphuric acid. The resulting droplets are very small, and so can remain in the stratosphere for several years. In contrast, the dust produced during a typical eruption is quite large and falls out of the atmosphere fairly quickly. For example, almost all the dust from the massive eruption of Mount Agung in 1963 seems to have been removed from the stratosphere within about six months.

An asteroid impact – unlike a volcanic eruption – would not produce sulphuric acid droplets, so direct comparisons based on the total amount of material injected into the atmosphere could be misleading. On the other hand, dust particles raised by an impact would probably be similar in size to volcanic dust, so the processes affecting them in the atmosphere would probably be similar. Particles in the lower atmosphere would soon fall to the ground by themselves or be washed out by rainfall. Dust thrown directly into the stratosphere would take longer to reach the ground, but the larger grains would fall out within a few weeks, and even submicron-sized particles could not remain aloft for more than about a year. Based on the analogy with volcanic dust, it seems that most of the dust from an asteroid impact is unlikely to remain in the air for more than a few months and almost all of it would probably settle within a year. This is a considerably shorter period than that envisaged by Alvarez in his original estimate.

Another important difference between impacts and eruptions is that the dust is likely to spread around the world in a totally different way. Dust from volcanic eruptions is spread by stratospheric winds which blow predominantly parallel to the equator. These winds can produce a band of volcanic dust around the world within a few weeks, but any movement in the North–South direction tends to be much slower. It took about nine months for material from the Mount Agung eruption to spread from its origin 9° south of the equator to the South Pole, and hardly any of its dust ever reached the northern hemisphere. Ejecta from an asteroid impact would probably behave quite differently. So much energy would be dumped into the stratosphere by the crater-forming explosion that the normal stratospheric winds would be upset and a totally abnormal circulation pattern would be set up for a time.

Studies based on the global dust storms observed on the planet Mars, whose entire atmosphere has about the same amount of gas as the Earth's stratosphere, suggest that the dust from an asteroid impact could be spread around the world much more quickly than volcanic dust – perhaps within a couple of weeks or less.

These results suggest that Alvarez's group were correct in their belief that an asteroid dust cloud could spread around the globe quite rapidly, but probably overestimated the time the cloud could remain in the atmosphere. None the less, the most important question about the implications of a global dust cloud on the life below is not how long asteroidal dust could remain in the atmosphere, but how effective it would be at blocking out the sunlight. Alvarez tried to estimate the period of global darkness by scaling up the effect of the Krakatoa explosion but, as we saw above, direct comparisons with volcanic eruptions can be misleading. Since then, computer simulations have been used to make more detailed calculations of the effects of large quantities of dust on atmospheric transparency. These have shown that for about three months after the impact – the exact duration depending on the amount of dust injected in the atmosphere – there is a very considerable reduction in the amount of light reaching the Earth's surface. Most of the simulations predict that for several months the daytime sky would be darker than normal moonlight, and it is quite likely that in the weeks immediately following the impact it would be so dark that normal vision would be impossible. The simulations also showed that these effects are unlikely to persist for more than a year, even after a very large impact.

There have been various attempts to calculate the effects of a global blackout on the ability of plants to produce food by photosynthesis. One of these used mathematical techniques developed to study the effects of modern airborne pollutants on agricultural productivity. These showed that a mass of only a few tens of millions of tonnes injected into the stratosphere would be enough to reduce the amount of energy suitable for photosynthesis to below a tenth of 1 per cent. This corresponds to the amount of dust injected into the stratosphere by quite a small asteroid impact; an object half the size of the asteroid proposed by Alvarez would probably be large enough. Such a cloud – if it could remain in the stratosphere for a period of several months – would probably have a catastrophic effect on many types of vegetation. Particularly vulnerable to such a crisis would be the tiny green plants which float in the ocean and are collectively called phytoplankton, the first link in the oceanic food chain.

What would be the effects of a global blackout on the oceanic food supply? The first would be to stop the phytoplankton from producing food or from reproducing, but the darkness would not immediately affect the population of tiny herbivorous animals which make up the zooplankton. Indeed, since many types of zooplankton feed at night, the low light levels might well cause them to continue feeding at their normal rate. Unfortunately – since the reproduction of the phytoplankton would have stopped – grazing by the zooplankton would cause the population of phytoplankton to fall very rapidly. This would mean that the food supply for the zooplankton would soon be exhausted, and before long they would be in imminent danger of starvation.

The response of plankton to a reduction in food supply depends on a number of factors: for example whether they are equipped to deal with normal seasonal changes. Modern plankton communities living in the polar or temperate oceans have adapted to survive the long winter periods of reduced sunlight. To them the effects of a short blackout during winter months might not be disastrous – calculations suggest that it would take more than three months of total darkness before the zooplankton began to die of starvation. The consequences of a similiar darkening during the summer, when the plankton are more active, might be much more serious: supplies of food for the zooplankton would be exhausted in about a third of the time. Bearing in mind that the seasons of the two hemispheres of the world are different by six months, it appears that for global destruction of large quantities of modern temperate oceanic plankton, a worldwide blackout of at least three months would be necessary.

Of course, Late Cretaceous plankton were not identical to modern temperate varieties because – amongst other things – the oceans were much warmer 65,000,000 years ago than they are today. Cretaceous plankton probably resembled modern tropical species, whose metabolic processes operate more quickly than

141

their cousins living in colder temperate or polar waters. This means that the plankton of the Late Cretaceous would have been less able than most modern types to survive a period of reduced food supply, even though ancient varieties living away from the equator would probably have adapted to seasonal darkenings during the winter months. It seems that a global blackout – whatever its cause – capable of stopping photosynthesis for several months is consistent with the mass extinctions of plankton at the Cretaceous-Tertiary boundary, and would probably have led to the other marine extinctions at about the same time.

The Late Cretaceous extinction was not confined to the oceans. It also affected land animals and plants, although less severely. Global darkness would have killed some terrestrial plants, but as we saw earlier many species would survive by restricting growth during the darkness or by growing again from seed after the sunlight returned. During the blackout large carnivorous animals would have found prey more difficult to locate, but the total amount of biological material on the land is considerably greater than in the oceans, and it would take some time before all the available food could have been consumed. Starvation does not appear to have been the primary cause of the extinctions on the land.

An alternative possibility is that the land extinctions were caused by the effects of stratospheric dust on the temperature. By restricting the amount of sunlight reaching the ground, a global dust layer would cause a worldwide temperature fall. In the case of the oceans, which have a large heat capacity, temperatures would fall only a few degrees, but on the continents temperatures would soon drop below freezing and these sub-zero conditions would probably last for about twice as long as the period of darkness. Provided temperatures did not fall too low, land plants would probably survive as they survive winter, but animals not adapted to long cold spells would perish. If this was the case, many species of small land animals may have survived because they were able to protect themselves against the cold by burrowing a few centimetres below the ground.

Overall it seems quite possible that large amounts of dust in the stratosphere could block out the sunlight for several months and that a cloud raised by an asteroid impact could have caused a collapse of the ecological balance at the end of the Cretaceous period. Although this might seem to confirm the impact hypothesis, it does not; all it shows is that an asteroid impact cannot be ruled out as the cause of the extinctions. Just because a global darkening could have occurred does not mean that it did, and even if there was a blackout it does not follow – despite the evidence of the iridium layer – that it was necessarily due to a cosmic impact.

Faced with a choice between a number of alternative theories for the Late Cretaceous mass extinction, most scientists will prefer the one which involves the fewest unproved assumptions. This is usually known as applying Occam's razor, but it could also be called the 'principle of least astonishment'. In particular, any theory which requires a one-off event of very low probability – like an asteroid impact – to explain at a stroke the wide range of extinctions at the Cretaceous-Tertiary boundary is sure to be regarded with some scepticism. To convince the world that such an event did occur, supporters of the impact hypothesis must first show that an asteroid impact fits all the observed facts, and then prove that no more conservative explanation (for example a gradual change in the climate) will do.

The most convincing evidence for an impact would be to find a large crater formed at the time of the Late Cretaceous extinction. Since no such crater has been identified, the only way to demonstrate that there was an impact is in a series of separate steps, built one upon another like a house of cards. If any one of the steps turns out to be false, then the whole idea will collapse. The first step is to confirm that the excess iridium in the boundary between Cretaceous and Tertiary strata is found all over the world. If it is not, then there can have been no global dust cloud. Secondly, it must be proved that the excess iridium is extra-terrestrial in origin. If it is not, an asteroid impact can be ruled out. Thirdly, there must be no possibility that the iridium is normal meteoritic material built up over a long period and somehow concentrated in the boundary layer. If the iridium could have been built up slowly, then no sudden catastrophe is necessary to explain it. Finally, the layer of iridium must coincide exactly with the time of the mass extinction and the extinctions must have occurred in a

143

very short time.

The first of these steps – the presence of excess iridium at the Cretaceous-Tertiary boundary all over the world – is quite easy to check. Samples of material from locations as far apart as Italy, Denmark, the South Atlantic seabed, the USA, the Pacific Ocean floor, New Zealand and the Soviet Union have been tested by a number of different scientists. Almost all the sites showed evidence of excess iridium at the Cretaceous-Tertiary boundary, and samples from Montana, USA, also contain shocked quartz crystals which resemble material found near impact craters. The impact hypothesis thus passes the first hurdle. There does appear to be a worldwide layer of iridium at the Cretaceous-Tertiary boundary, and there is some evidence that it is associated with impact ejecta. Unfortunately, even after allowing for the effects of continental drift, there is no sign of any global trend in the amount of excess iridium which might provide a clue to the location of the impact site.

The second question – whether the iridum is extraterrestrial – is rather harder to answer. As we saw earlier, if the ratio of iridium isotopes within the clay was very different to the ratio found elsewhere on the Earth, this would indicate that it came from outside the solar system. Unfortunately, isotopic ratios cannot distinguish between terrestrial and asteroidal (or cometary) material, provided it was originally part of the same interstellar cloud from which the solar system condensed.

If the boundary clay contained a mixture of elements in a combination typical of meteorites but unlike normal terrestrial rocks, this would be strong circumstantial evidence for an extraterrestrial origin. Unfortunately, during an impact large quantities of target rock are exploded out of the crater along with the bolide material, so the composition of the projectile is extremely difficult to separate from the terrestrial fallout. Alvarez believes that the ratios of gold and platinum to iridium in the boundary clays are sufficiently different from terrestrial rocks to provide an elemental fingerprint of the asteroid. Based on these ratios, he suggests that the asteroid was similar to a very common type of stony meteorite known as a chondrite.

Other scientists do not accept this conclusion. By examining the

144

isotopic ratios of various other elements in the layers marking the Cretaceous-Tertiary boundary, a number of different groups have concluded that the material could have come either from meteorites or from below the Earth's crust. Examination of the ratios of iridium to antimony and arsenic in the boundary layer leads to a more definite conclusion: these ratios are thousands of times too low to have come from a chondritic meteorite. Furthermore, the clay itself does not seem to contain any unusual minerals which mark it as being profoundly different from similar clay layers above and below the Cretaceous-Tertiary boundary. The suggestion that the clay contains a considerable fraction of asteroidal material can apparently be ruled out, although two different groups – which obtained similar results on the composition of the clay – came to quite opposite conclusions about its origin, one supporting and the other rejecting the impact hypothesis.

Since attempts to prove that the material in the boundary layer is extraterrestrial have proved inconclusive, we must seek an alternative approach to the problem. For example, if there is no normal geological process by which large quantities of terrestrial iridium could be propelled into the stratosphere, then an extraterrestrial origin would be the only other possibility. Alvarez based his suggestion of an asteroid impact on the fact that iridium is very rare in the Earth's crust, but the isotopic studies described above suggest that iridium might have come from below the crust, and been injected into the atmosphere by volcanoes.

Dramatic support for this suggestion has recently come from a group of scientists studying the volcanoes in the Hawaiian islands. They discovered that fine particles ejected from the volcano Kilauea contained tens of thousands of times more iridium than was found in the solidified lava which makes up the island itself. If the airborne particles from Kilauea are typical of other volcanoes, then volcanic iridium in the atmosphere would be about as common as iridium burned off meteorites. A volcanic origin for the boundary-clay iridium does seem to be a possibility, especially since much of the Danish Fish Clay sediment is composed of the mineral smectite, which can be produced from material originating in volcanoes. Significantly, the ratios of antimony, arsenic and iridium in the dust from Kilauea are reasonably similar to those in the Cretaceous-Tertiary clays.

Further support for a volcanic origin for the iridium comes from the presence of tiny glassy spheres, generally less than a tenth of a millimetre in size, in the clay at a number of different locations. Similar spherules occur in other clay layers and these are known to have been laid over a period of more than 20,000,000 years. They cannot all have come from a single impact. There is no doubt that spherules of this type are formed during volcanic eruptions; there are examples from a number of modern volcanoes. This suggests that around the time of the Late Cretaceous mass extinction there may have been a sudden burst of volcanic activity which produced both the iridium excess and the concentration of spherules in the boundary clay.

What of the evidence from Montana that the iridium in the boundary clay is accompanied by quartz that has been shocked by an impact? Traces of highly shocked minerals have been found in material ejected from the ancient volcano of Toba, in Sumatra. This huge volcano has undergone at least three major eruptions during the last million years and the most recent, about 75,000 years ago, was much more powerful than the eruption of Krakatoa in 1883. The discovery shows that exceptionally large volcanic eruptions can produce shocked material which resembles ejecta from a large impact crater, ruling out the need for an impact to explain the presence of shocked quartz in Montana.

One other piece of evidence points to a volcanic, rather than asteroidal, origin for the iridium. Although there is no known impact crater 65,000,000 years old, there are clear signs of considerable volcanic activity at the end of the Cretaceous. This evidence is found in India in the region known as the Deccan Traps, where 500,000 square kilometres of land are covered by an estimated 1,000,000 cubic kilometres of lava – material which has risen to the surface from below the Earth's crust. The flooding of this enormous area was not instantaneous – it probably took over 70,000,000 years altogether – but we know that most of the activity happened during a fairly short period between 60 and 65 million years ago. We do not know the precise duration of this volcanic episode, but it almost certainly lasted for less than a million years. Alvarez and his group are undaunted by this evidence. They believe that the iridium in the boundary clay was laid down in a much shorter period, and restate their view that the elements in the clay point to an asteroidal impact, blasting through the crust, which triggered the vulcanism in India.

To summarize: we cannot prove that the iridium in the boundary clays is extraterrestrial, and a conventional geological explanation for its presence is available. None the less, the impact hypothesis can survive these criticisms provided Alvarez and his colleagues are correct in their view that the iridium was laid down over a very short period; according to them, volcanic activity cannot lay down the iridium in the boundary clay fast enough.

Attention now focuses on the third question: How quickly was the iridium layer deposited, and could it have been concentrated at the boundary, giving a false impression of a sudden deposition? At the original sites used for the investigations the precise lengths of time the boundary clay layer took to form is difficult to measure. All that we can say is that it was rapid compared with normal geological events. Further measurements by other scientists using samples from southern Spain have shown that on average the sedimentary rocks in Spain were laid down at a rate of about one millimetre per 26 years. Since the iridium in this region is concentrated in a layer only about one millimetre thick, it was probably deposited in less than 50 years. This rapid fallout provides strong support for the impact hypothesis.

It is difficult to measure such small time intervals precisely because animals which live at the bottom of the sea and burrow into the mud on the sea floor inevitably churn up the sediment before it can harden into rock. This smears out the very fine structure in individual layers of rock, destroying any evidence for very short periods of deposition. A closer examination of the iridium anomaly over the whole world indicates that – allowing for mixing by sea-floor burrowers – the boundary material was indeed laid down very quickly in some places, but at others deposition seems to have been a gradual process lasting between 10,000 and 100,000 years. Once again the results are inconclusive, with evidence both for and against rapid deposition.

All the debate over how long it took the iridium to be deposited is based on the assumption that it was not concentrated at the boundary by some sort of chemical process. Alvarez and his group rejected this as implausible, but since then other scientists have suggested methods which could produce such an enrichment. One of these is based on the fact that much of the material falling to the seabed is the shells of tiny marine creatures. These shells are composed of calcium carbonate, which is soluble in slightly acidic water and is the principal component of limestone. It is only because the oceans are saturated with calcium carbonate and cannot dissolve any more that the shells survive long enough to be incorporated into sedimentary rocks. The non-catastrophic explanation for the iridium anomaly assumes that the boundary clay was originally mixed in amongst a much thicker layer of limestone. If there then was a gradual change in the ocean chemistry for some reason – perhaps connected with the lowering of the sea level known to have occurred during the Late Cretaceous – the limestone could be dissolved away, leaving the insoluble clay to sink to the sea floor. This would produce the abnormally high iridium concentration observed at the boundary. If substantiated, this suggestion would be fatal to the impact theory since the iridium in the boundary clay would then be caused by the normal influx of meteoritic (or volcanic) iridium, artifically concentrated in the boundary when the limestone dissolved.

Changes in ocean chemistry could not, of course, explain an iridium anomaly in material laid down on dry land rather than on the sea floor. Since most of the samples originally analysed for iridium were ancient ocean-floor material, Alvarez and his group set out to find evidence of an anomaly in non-marine sediments. At first they believed they had succeeded: a non-marine sample from Montana appeared to contain large quantities of iridium, but further analysis of material from this site failed to confirm the discovery. There was a search to find the reason for this disparity. The problem was eventually traced to contamination from the platinum wedding ring of a laboratory technician. Platinum used in jewellery manufacture contains about 10 per cent iridium; apparently, tiny flakes from the ring were getting into the rock samples and distorting the results. Alvarez admits to being embarrassed by this accident, but it does illustrate, if nothing else, the fantastic power of modern geochemical techniques and the tiny concentrations of material detectable during the analysis. Fortunately for supporters of the impact hypothesis, another group subsequently found a non-marine iridium anomaly in the American state of New Mexico.

Once again, we can draw no definite conclusions from these results. The iridium may have been deposited quickly – or it may not have been. Chemical methods could produce the anomaly in ocean sediments – but apparently not on dry land. The impact hypothesis is not confirmed – nor can it be ruled out. The final question is: Did the extinctions at the Cretaceous-Tertiary boundary take place over hundreds or thousands of years, or were they virtually instantaneous? Once again, this is controversial territory.

The main difficulty is that the fossil record is simply not accurate enough to distinguish between an event which happened almost overnight and one which lasted many decades. This is because different sediments are laid down at different rates, and currents and sea-floor creatures disrupt sediment layers before the seabed solidifies. There are also subtle selection effects in the number and type of fossils available for analysis. In general, palaeontologists do not personally dig up every fossil they use in their research; like all scientists, they rely on the work of others published in scientific journals. Often the original work may have been done for some quite different purpose, so careful interpretation is required before reaching any conclusions. To give just one example: collections of animal fossils are heavily biased towards large creatures like dinosaurs, rather than their smaller contemporaries. This does not imply that there were lots more large creatures than small ones; it simply shows that most museums prefer big skeletons which make spectacular displays to case after case of tiny fossils which are barely distinguishable to the lay visitor. Such problems are compounded by the difficulty of comparing the fossil record from place to place and relating the time of events in the oceans to those on land.

Many thousands of words have been written, and whole scientific conferences have been dedicated, to trying to solve the question of whether or not the Late Cretaceous extinctions occurred quickly. No clear conclusions have yet been reached.

There is certainly no doubt that there was a massive destruction of marine life about 65,000,000 years ago; it is equally certain that many land animals died out at about the same time. What is far from clear is whether the land and sea extinctions happened within a few weeks or months of each other, as required by the basic impact hypothesis. Many palaeontologists believe that the two events were separated by a much longer period, possibly as many as several hundred thousand years. Such a long-drawn-out period – combined with the selectivity of the extinctions (dinosaurs died, but crocodiles survived) – would point to a gradually operating cause, not a catastrophe. Supporters of the impact hypothesis counter this by suggesting that the impact was responsible for the oceanic extinctions and these in turn led to environmental changes, such as a build-up of carbon dioxide in the atmosphere, which caused climatic changes resulting in the rest of the extinctions. The evidence is probably so ambiguous that we shall never know that true answer.

Where does this leave the impact hypothesis? Most palaeontologists do not accept the view that the mass extinctions were either very rapid or simultaneous. Since the idea of a gradual extinction, probably due to climatic change, has been popular for many years this could be seen as a manifestation of the principle of least astonishment – but there is no evidence to prove that the extinctions were very rapid. The impact hypothesis requires that the extinctions were sudden – but the fossil record does not require a catastrophe, although it does not unambiguously exclude one. If fossilized dinosaurs could be found above the iridium layer, the impact hypothesis would be in serious trouble – but only one such set of fossils has been found, and the dating of these samples has been challenged.

Overall it seems that the impact hypothesis is 'not proven'. Its supporters will need to produce more convincing evidence before it is accepted, or its detracters must find some as yet undetected fatal flaw. One possibility is that both viewpoints are partly correct. Perhaps the Late Cretaceous ecology was already in decline when an asteroid impact delivered the *coup de grâce* and accelerated the final collapse. In any event, the iridium in the

Cretaceous-Tertiary boundary clay cries out for an explanation and the research stimulated by the controversy has greatly added to our understanding of asteroid impacts. Whatever killed the dinosaurs, there are many other unanswered questions about the role of cosmic impacts on the history of the Earth.

7

Cosmic Cycles?

It is still an open question whether or not the extinctions which occurred at the Cretaceous-Tertiary boundary were caused by a cosmic impact. One thing, however, is clear; an asteroid impact is not the catch-all answer to the questions posed by mass extinctions. Even so, two key points about impacts seem to have been established beyond much doubt:

Large asteroids and comets have struck the Earth a number of times since life developed on our planet.

The biological consequences of a major impact must have been severe.

Unless one of these conclusions is hopelessly wrong, there should be some biological catastrophes which are unambiguously linked with impacts; it only remains to find them. The obvious place to look for a link is at the geological boundaries which mark the other great extinctions, and there have already been several searches at different sites around the world.

In an attempt to confirm their belief in a link between impacts and extinctions, Alvarez and his group examined two other geological levels for any sign of excess iridium. The boundaries chosen were the Late Permian mass extinction of 240,000,000 years ago, and a period about 34,000,000 years ago which is known as the Eocene-Oligocene boundary.

The Late Permian boundary was picked because it marks by far the greatest known mass extinction, with an enormous number of species vanishing. Despite the extinctions' scale, this is an unusual place to search for evidence of an impact because, as we saw in Chapter 6, the Late Permian extinctions probably took place over a period lasting several million years. Such a long-drawn-out event points to gradually operating causes such as climatic changes associated with (for example) an episode of massive continental drift or a fall in sea level, not to a sudden global catastrophe.

Perhaps not surprisingly, the layers marking the end of the Permian contained no excess iridium, nor did they contain any evidence of other extraterrestrial material. The composition of the boundary layer itself was different from the layers immediately above and below, but in the absence of excess iridium this was attributed to a period of prolonged volcanic activity at the same time as the large-scale continental drift at the end of the Permian.

As if reluctant to abandon the impact hypothesis, Alvarez and his group did hint that a comet, rather than an asteroid, might have been responsible for the extinctions. This suggestion is based on the fact that a long-period comet would be travelling faster than an asteroid when it struck the Earth, and a smaller impacting object could produce an explosion of the same energy. Furthermore a comet, which is composed mostly of ice, would contain much less iridium than a stony asteroid. A suitable comet impact could produce all the effects required to cause an extinction, and yet deposit so little extraterrestrial iridium in the boundary layer that it would be undetectable with existing techniques. This is a valid point, but there is so much evidence suggesting that the extinctions were gradual that it seems rather pointless to postulate the impact of a comet for which there is no evidence.

The decision to search for iridium near the Eocene-Oligocene boundary – even though this is not recognized as the time of a mass extinction – was based upon two factors. Five species of single-celled marine creatures died out simultaneously about 2,000,000 years before the end of the Eocene, and these extinctions seem to have occurred at the same time as the arrival of a massive shower of tektites. As we saw in Chapter 4, tektites are small, glassy stones which are probably solidified droplets of molten rock flung out during the formation of a large impact crater. The tektites which landed near the end of the Eocene, including microtektites found in sediments from the ocean floor, are spread over half of the world – the total mass of the shower has been estimated as 10,000 million tonnes. The presence of such a large field of tektites strongly suggests that there was a major cosmic impact somewhere in the world about 36,000,000 years ago. There is no large crater of this age on land, so the object presumably landed in the ocean.

The search for iridium in the sediments associated with the microtektites was successful: there was about 20 times more than expected. Once again, the relative concentration of iridium to other elements was used as evidence that the iridium was extraterrestrial, and as with the Cretaceous-Tertiary boundary clay, the possibility that the iridium was burned off meteorites over a long period was rejected. The coincidence of excess iridium and microtektites was not exact, but small glassy spheres related to the microtektites were found alongside the iridium and the displacement of the remaining microtektites from the iridium was attributed to disturbances in the sea-floor mud caused by bottom-dwelling creatures.

The presence of excess iridium in layers of sediment laid down close to the end of the Eocene has since been confirmed, and there have been attempts to estimate the size of the impacting object. Based on the extent of the tektite field and the concentration of excess iridium, the asteroid was probably about 3 kilometres across. This is much smaller than the object proposed for the Late Cretaceous extinctions, and would presumably explain why its effects were less severe. The extinctions in the ocean do not, for example, appear to have been matched on land. There were a number of extinctions of terrestrial mammals about 2,000,000 years after the tektites were laid down, and it is these extinctions which mark the internationally recognized boundary between the Eocene and the Oligocene. Unless, however, there is a serious mismatch between the dating of the land and ocean extinctions it is unlikely that these are connected to the suggested asteroid impact.

The American astronomer John O'Keefe has put forward an alternative possibility linking the tektites to the biological and climatic changes at the end of the Eocene. He believes that the tektites originated on the Moon – a view not shared by most other astronomers – and were shot out of lunar volcanoes. O'Keefe suggests that as well as the tektites which fell directly on to the Earth, a huge number were injected into orbit round our planet, forming rings like those around Saturn. These rings would cast a shadow over part of the Earth, always affecting the winter hemisphere of the planet. (This is because the rings would revolve in the plane of the Moon's orbit, which is quite close to the Earth's equator, but the equator is tilted over with respect to the Earth's orbit around the Sun. So when the Sun is south of the equator – i.e. it is winter in the northern hemisphere – the ring shadow falls on northerly latitudes, but when the Sun is north of the equator – i.e. it is winter in the south – the shadow falls in the southern hemisphere.)

These rings would produce severe winters. O'Keefe calculated that they would be 20°C colder than usual; summers would be normal, or even warmer than average. These effects would persist until the rings had been dissipated by atmospheric drag which, although small, affects particles in low orbit, causing them to spiral down towards the Earth. The discovery that the tektites laid down just before the end of the Eocene are associated with what appears to be extraterrestrial iridium – while the tektites themselves contain no excess iridium – implies that the tektites are terrestrial rock thrown up by an extraterrestrial impact. This has cast considerable doubt on O'Keefe's rather imaginative idea, and few astronomers now believe that the Earth was ever a ringed planet.

Searches for evidence of excess iridium at other boundaries associated with mass extinctions have not been conclusive. In 1984 two different groups reported the results of their search for an iridium anomaly at the Frasnian-Famennian boundary. One group failed to find any excess iridium in samples taken from sites in the USA and in Belgium; the other did find iridium at a site in Australia. Both groups went on to hedge their bets, the first by stating that the extinction might have been caused by the impact of a body containing little or no iridium – for example a comet – the second by pointing out that the iridium could have been concentrated by biological processes, and did not necessarily imply an asteroid impact. To add to the confusion, yet another group has discovered an iridium anomaly in a sample from the floor of the Antarctic Ocean and the time this iridium was deposited does not appear to coincide with any sudden extinctions.

Despite the uncertainties surrounding attempts to link specific

155

extinctions to individual impacts, the intellectual climate for theories of evolution by catastrophe has changed. By the early 1980s there was a growing body of evidence – albeit controversial – for two episodes of impact-related extinctions, and attempts to link extraterrestrial forces and evolution were acceptable, even fashionable. The scene was set for a new explosion of ideas relating comets and catastrophe.

The spark for this explosion was provided by David Raup and J. John Sepkoski, both from the University of Chicago, who suggested that mass extinctions occurred with almost clockwork regularity. Raup and Sepkoski used an extensive collection of data on 3500 types of ancient marine animals, covering 250,000,000 years of evolution, and looked for patterns in the time of extinctions. To avoid being misled by factors which might affect one group of organisms more severely than others, their sample included a range of vertebrates, invertebrates and single-celled creatures. Their search was successful, and in 1984 they reported that large numbers of extinctions seemed to take place every 26,000,000 years. Raup and Sepkoski went on to say that because biological causes for this periodicity seemed implausible, astronomical forces were probably at work.

Such a conclusion was not new; claims of periodicity in the fossil record had been made before, but two things made this one different. Firstly, Raup and Sepkoski had taken care to guard against the many pitfalls which can distort this kind of analysis, and secondly – thanks to Luis and Walter Alvarez – the scientific world was more receptive to their conclusions. In fact, it was so receptive that almost before Raup and Sepkoski could publish their results a number of scientists were leaping forward with suggestions to explain this cycle of catastrophe.

Almost all the ideas involved periodic bombardments of the Earth from space, and one of the first to seize on Raup and Sepkoski's results was Walter Alvarez who, with Richard Muller, examined the record of terrestrial craters between five and 250 million years old. They excluded very young craters from their analysis because there is a comparatively large number and they might upset the statistical balance of the sample. Also, since they expected a periodicity of about 26,000,000 years from the pattern of extinctions, they also excluded any crater whose age was uncertain by more than 20,000,000 years. Rejecting these craters was an essential safeguard against finding a false pattern in the data, because a crater whose age was very uncertain might fit into any number of patterns, real or imaginary. They then analysed their sample of craters and found that the impacts seemed to occur at intervals of 28.4 million years.

After allowing for the uncertainties in the crater ages and in the precise dates of the mass extinctions, it seemed that the peaks in the cycle of impacts came at the same time as the extinctions, which strongly suggested that they were directly connected. Alvarez and Muller estimated that the chance of this agreement being coincidental was one in a thousand, but there was one problem: the periodicity of the craters suggested that there should have been two mass extinctions in the period between about 150 and 200 million years ago, but the fossil record appears to show three comparatively minor ones. Rather than abandon their theory of periodic impacts, Alvarez and Muller suggested that the record of extinctions was poorly defined in this time interval and that it was errors in the dates of the extinctions that led to the mismatch.

At first sight this evidence for periodic impacts coinciding with mass extinctions seems quite impressive, although it gives no clue to the cause of the regular bombardments. The results should, however, be interpreted cautiously. In particular, they are based on only 13 craters which qualify for selection, and statistical analysis of small samples can often produce misleading data. The problem of the mismatch between the two cycles also remains unexplained.

Other astronomers took a different approach to the problems raised by Raup and Sepkoski: rather than trying to relate the extinctions to specific impact craters, they simply took the periodicity of mass extinctions for granted and looked for possible astronomical explanations. Since the effects of impacts seemed the most likely extraterrestrial cause of the extinctions, the problem was to discover the nature of the projectiles and to explain why they should strike the Earth in such a regular pattern.

At the moment, collisions between Apollo asteroids and the Earth occur at random and there is no obvious way the present population of Apollos could be marshalled to produce a regular cycle of impacts. None the less, before periodic asteroid impacts can be rejected we must examine the possibility that the number of Apollos today is not typical of the population in the past. We saw in Chapter 3 that the number of craters on the Moon and planets implies that there are about twice as many more Apollos today than are necessary to produce the observed cratering by a gradual bombardment throughout the history of the solar system. Because of this, some astronomers believe that the present Apollos are the last survivors of a much larger population which was responsible for the last periodic bombardment of the Earth. In practice, there is much uncertainty in the calculations of both the cratering rates and the numbers of Earth-crossing asteroids, and a difference of a factor of two between the figures is probably not very significant. On balance, there seems no convincing reason to suggest that the number of Apollo asteroids has varied very dramatically over the last few hundred million years, so regular asteroid impacts are unlikely to have caused periodic mass extinctions.

With asteroids eliminated, the most likely explanation for a periodic bombardment of the Earth must be a variation in the number of comets entering the inner solar system. Some astronomers believe that Apollo asteroids are burnt-out short-period comets and extend this idea to suggest that members of these comet showers are first trapped into Earth-crossing orbits and then evolve into Apollo objects, but in either case, a source of regular and dramatic showers must be found. Apart from a small number of short-period comets which stay quite close to the Sun and are seen regularly, the vast majority of comets reside in the Oort cloud and under normal circumstances it is small random gravitational tugs by nearby stars which stir them up and send a few towards the Sun each year. To produce the comet showers required to explain the periodicity in the mass extinctions, we need something that can influence the Oort cloud in a regular fashion, throwing extra comets towards the Earth in huge numbers. This extra influence could be the gravitational attraction of an unknown companion to the Sun – either a distant planet or a small, faint star.

The idea that the Sun has a tenth planet beyond Pluto is popular (although there is virtually no evidence to support it), and there are theoretical reasons to suppose that there is a disc of comets – forming a sort of inner Oort cloud – somewhere beyond the orbit of Neptune. Under rather special circumstances this hypothetical 'Planet X' could influence an inner disc of comets and produce regular comet showers. Planet X need not be very large – one calculation suggests not much bigger than the Earth – but it would need to be more distant than Pluto and travelling in an eccentric orbit inclined at a considerable angle to the rest of the planets. In such an orbit Planet X would spend most of its time far above or below the disc of comets, and could have no significant influence on the number of comets entering the solar system.

Occasionally, when Planet X was at the distance of the comet disc and also happened to be close to its plane, its gravity would disturb the cometary orbits and send huge numbers of comets falling in towards Jupiter. Encounters with Jupiter would then send some of them into Earth-crossing orbits closer to the Sun. During each of these encounters with Planet X zones in the inner disc of comets would be swept clear, so astronomically speaking the shower would be quite short, lasting only about a million years. The showers could occur only when the relative positions of Planet X and the comet disc were correct, and because of the eccentric and highly inclined orbit of the planet this would happen infrequently. There would therefore be long intervals between comet showers. During these intervals, the gradual stirring up of comets in the Oort cloud by other stars would allow new comets to move into the danger zone ready for the next disruptive encounter with Planet X. The time between showers would depend on the exact orbit of Planet X, and an orbit producing a 26,000,000-year cycle of bombardment is quite possible.

As an alternative to an explanation requiring both a tenth planet and an inner disc of comets – neither of which has ever been seen – other scientists proposed that the comet showers were produced by the effects of a faint stellar companion to the Sun on the Oort cloud (strictly speaking no one has ever seen the main Oort cloud either, but most astronomers do accept that it exists). Systems containing two stars orbiting around each other are quite common, and pairs containing stars of widely different brightness are not unusual, so it is possible that the Sun has an as yet undiscovered faint companion. To explain the periodic extinctions the proposed companion star would need to be in an eccentric orbit stretching about 100,000 AU from the Sun, making one orbit every 26,000,000 years. On each trip around the Sun the star would pass through the Oort cloud and send millions of comets towards the inner solar system, leading to a dramatic bombardment of the Earth lasting a few hundred thousand years.

The size of the companion star depends on both the details of its orbit and the density of comets within the Oort cloud, but it is probably less than 1 per cent of the mass of the Sun. A star this small would never get hot enough to produce energy by nuclear reactions and so would be quite cool, radiating much of its energy not as light but as infra-red radiation. Such tiny stars are called brown, or black, dwarfs and are extremely difficult to find, even when they are very close to the Sun, so it would not be surprising if a solar companion of this type had not yet been detected.

Two different groups simultaneously suggested the existence of a brown dwarf companion to the Sun as a means of producing comet showers, and both came up with roughly the same values for its size and orbit. One even went so far as to propose that should it ever be discovered, the object should be named 'Nemesis' after the Greek goddess who persecuted the rich and powerful. Although few astronomers are rich and powerful, this group added that if the star was never located, their calculations might prove to be their own nemesis. They added, reassuringly, that at the moment Nemesis would be very distant from the Sun, and would present no further danger to the Earth before about AD 15,000,000. Other astronomers prefer to call this hypothetical solar companion 'The Death Star', a name drived from a well-known science fiction film.

Despite its instinctive appeal there are a number of problems facing the Death Star theory. The most important concerns the stability of the orbit the star must follow to produce the observed pattern of extinctions. At the most distant point in its orbit, Nemesis would be a very long way from the solar system. At such a large distance the Sun's gravitational attraction is very weak and there is a good chance that Nemesis would fall under the influence of another star. Although the pull of this star might not be strong enough to drag Nemesis away from the Sun in one go, it would certainly be able to modify its orbit. Calculations have shown that, because of the attraction of other stars, the orbit calculated for Nemesis is unstable. It could not remain bound to the Sun for more than a few hundred million years.

This implies either that Nemesis was originally a separate star which was somehow captured by the Sun, or that it was once bound more closely to the solar system and has moved into its present orbit only within the last 100,000,000 years or so. Likelihood of capture of another star by the Sun is less than one in a million million so, if it exists, Nemesis must have been pulled outwards from the Sun quite recently. Such a dramatic change in the orbit of a solar companion is possible. The galaxy contains – as well as stars – huge gas clouds each as massive as half a million Suns. The gravitational pull of one of these could easily pull Nemesis into a new orbit. There is still much debate as to whether or not an encounter with a giant cloud could stretch the orbit of Nemesis by the required amount without stripping away all the comets in the Oort cloud at the same time. To add to these difficulties, the Sun has probably encountered a number of these giant clouds during its life, any one of which could have removed Nemesis completely, so a scenario in which the Death Star and the Oort cloud both survive these encounters to produce the conditions for periodic comet impacts seems rather contrived.

Even if the Death Star could survive the encounters with giant gas clouds, there is still a problem over its ability to produce regular bombardments of the Earth. The pull of nearby stars is strong enough to cause changes in the orbit of Nemesis almost every time it goes around the Sun. Changing the shape of its orbit would change its orbital period, destroying the regular periodicity required to produce the patterns of extinction reported by Raup and Sepkoski.

All these arguments are of necessity theoretical, because no faint solar companion has yet been found. The recent survey by the Infra-Red Astronomical Satellite (IRAS) may detect a number of brown dwarf stars near the Sun, one of which could turn out to be

161

in orbit around the solar system. Until such a star is detected, the Death Star hypothesis fails to keep to the principle of least astonishment and can probably be rejected.

The difficulties associated with the stability of a solar companion led to another explanation of the periodic mass extinctions, this time involving the effects of the Sun's motion through the galaxy. The hundred thousand million stars which make up our galaxy, the Milky Way, are concentrated in a rotating, flattened disc. The Sun, like many other stars, drifts up and down as the Milky Way rotates, passing through the galactic plane at regular intervals. A number of astronomers have speculated that passages through the galactic plane might be responsible for the reported cycles of catastrophe.

Michael Rampino and Richard Strothers re-examined the data used by Raup and Sepkoski to derive the 26,000,000-year period between mass extinctions, and came to a slightly different conclusion. Rampino and Strothers estimated the average period between extinctions to be about 30,000,000 years, with significant variations in the length of time from one event to another. Since this interval is similar to the time taken by the Sun to complete one of its cycles through the galactic plane, a connection seemed possible. Rampino and Strothers suggested that as most of the galaxy's gas and dust clouds are concentrated near the galactic plane, the chances that the Sun will have a close encounter with a cloud is greatest during the crossing, and the gravitational effects of the interstellar material on the Oort cloud could cause a comet shower. There would be variation in the intervals between extinctions because encounters with interstellar clouds do not take place exactly at the time the Sun crosses the galactic plane; some occur before the crossing and others just after.

Countering this suggestion (and others like it), astronomers have pointed out that although the clouds of gas and dust are concentrated towards the galactic plane, they are also found well above and below it, so encounters between the solar system and interstellar clouds would occur more or less at random. In any case, the last of the proposed extinctions happened when the Earth was well away from the galactic plane, not in the middle of it.

Galactic plane crossings, like solar companions, cannot provide a satisfactory explanation for cycles of bombardment.

Sometime before the discovery of periodicity in the record of extinctions, Victor Clube and Bill Napier put forward a similar proposal linking terrestrial catastrophes to encounters with interstellar clouds. Clube and Napier argued that an encounter with a giant interstellar cloud would strip most of the Oort cloud from the Sun. Since the solar system has had many such encounters during its history, there is virtually no chance that the comets which are observed today were part of the original system. From this, they suggested that the comets are probably formed inside the interstellar clouds and captured whenever the Sun encounters a cloud.

According to Clube and Napier, each encounter with a cloud has two effects. Firstly, most of the existing comets in the Oort cloud are removed and replaced by new ones from the cloud. Secondly, during the disruption of the Oort cloud there is a burst of comets into the inner solar system. These comets might include objects much larger than those observed today if the comets currently entering the solar system are merely the final members of a much larger shower which occurred a few million years ago. The capture of a number of these comets into Earth-crossing orbits would lead to a series of impact-induced catastrophes including vulcanism, climatic change and mass extinctions.

The time between encounters with interstellar clouds is probably between 100 and 200 million years, with near misses capable of causing smaller comet showers perhaps once every 50,000,000 years or so. Clube and Napier have developed this idea to provide an explanation for some of the Earth's legendary past catastrophes, and details of this work can be found in the Bibliography. Their suggestion that comets are of interstellar origin rather than part of the original solar system is not widely supported, but our present understanding of comets is so poor that it cannot be ruled out, and may yet turn out to be true.

At this point, a moment's reflection is called for. The search for the cause of periodic extinctions has progressed from asteroids to as yet undiscovered companions of the Sun, and out to involve the very fabric of the galaxy itself. In this headlong rush into space, could it be that something is being overlooked? Many scientists believe that this is so, and that the search for cosmic cycles has become a runaway bandwagon capable of carrying an almost infinite number of passengers. In particular, it seems that some basic principles of the scientific method are being sidestepped, even ignored completely. It is quite correct that a new idea should receive a fair hearing, but statements which imply that since the accepted facts do not fit the theory then the facts must be wrong cannot be allowed to pass unchallenged. To accept some of the arguments put forward by supporters of periodic impacts may be carrying an open mind a little too far.

Since none of the causes suggested to explain the regular periods of mass extinction seems to be entirely satisfactory, could there be a basic problem with the conclusion that there is in fact a regular cycle in the fossil record? The claims by Raup and Sepkoski for a cycle of mass extinctions have now come under considerable criticism on several grounds. For example, the reliability of the dates used in their analysis has been questioned. There are at least two widely used geological timescales, with differences between these systems. Raup and Sepkoski used one scale, which should be internally consistent, but if it turns out that there are major errors in this scale then the claimed periodicity will almost certainly vanish when the data is reanalysed. A further difficulty is the absolute accuracy of the ages applied to different stratigraphic levels. The dates assigned to individual levels more than about 100,000,000 years old may be out by 5,000,000 years or more. This leads to different ages being assigned to the same event, and raises further doubts on the reliability of the calculated periodicity.

Another criticism of the apparent cycles is based on the exact definition of a mass extinction. The Late Permian extinction involved hundreds of different types of creatures, but some of the more recent events described as mass extinctions involve much smaller numbers. Of the 12 events used by Raup and Sepkoski several are regarded by many palaeontologists as quite minor, and some do not fit the 26,000,000-year cycle very well. This reduces the number of valid mass extinctions in their data by almost half, rendering it rather small to use for rigorous statistical analysis. As evidence of this, one scientist at a recent conference went so far as to generate some hypothetical random cratering histories, and challenged the audience to try and distinguish the real sequence from one of the imaginary ones. One in five got it wrong.

The data used by Raup and Sepkoski have been edited to remove both families of creatures which are still extant today and others for which the time of extinction is not reliably known. This leads to fairly arbitrary decisions on what does or does not constitute valid data. Such decisions can, quite unconsciously, influence the periodicity found when the data are analysed. Other geologists have analysed the unedited version of the data and obtained quite different results. There was a hint of this problem earlier when we saw how Rampino and Strothers used the same data as Raup and Sepkoski and yet derived a rather different period between extinctions. If the periods were real then such ambiguity should not occur.

Overall, the burden of proof seems to lie on those who favour regular extinctions and much needs to be done before a Death Star – or any other astronomical cause – is necessary to explain the fossil record. The pattern of extinctions which requires cosmic cycles may be a matter of definitions, not disasters.

8

The Stone of Damocles

Whatever the connection between impacts and evolution, there is no doubt that asteroids do collide with our planet. What happened at Tunguska in 1908 shows that even a small Apollo object would produce a major disaster should it happen to fall on a densely populated area. Fortunately, the likelihood of even a small asteroid impact on a city during the lifetime of anyone reading this book is almost zero, and even if one came, mankind as a whole would not be threatened. Although locally disastrous, a small impact is unlikely to have any major ecological effects on the Earth.

None the less, it is interesting to speculate on the options open to mankind if we discovered a much larger asteroid on a collision course with the Earth. This is a theme popular with science fiction writers since H.G. Wells's book *The Star* was published in 1897, and it has featured in a number of more recent books and films. Our new understanding of the Apollo asteroids now makes it possible to assess what, if anything, could be done to prevent a catastrophic cosmic impact.

The critical factor would be how much time was available between the discovery of the asteroid and its cataclysmic arrival at the Earth. At the moment no Apollo asteroid is known to pose a threat to our planet, so any danger would have to come from an as yet undiscovered object. In such circumstances there are two possibilities: either the asteroid will impact very soon after its discovery, or it will present a threat to the Earth at some future date. As an example – and for comparison with the object proposed as the cause of the extinctions at the Cretaceous-Tertiary boundary – imagine an asteroid about 10 kilometres across, on a collision course with Earth, travelling with a relative velocity of about 20 kilometres per second.

In the first – and least likely – case it is fairly easy to estimate how close the asteroid could get before it would become bright

166

enough to be discovered by one of the regular asteroid search programmes described in Chapter 3. This distance will be only very approximate, because the brightness of the asteroid will depend on its surface composition and the relative positions of the asteroid, Earth and Sun, but it will at least provide some rough idea of the amount of warning the world might receive. In practice, there could be no warning at all, because if the asteroid were to approach close to an imaginary line joining Earth and Sun, it would never be visible in a night-time sky and would be quite impossible to discover with normal telescopes. Its arrival would come, literally, as a bolt from the blue.

Under more favourable circumstances the asteroid could be discovered when its brightness reached about fifteenth magnitude, which would mean that it was about 20,000,000 kilometres from the Earth. Of course, there is no guarantee that it would be found immediately; even the most dedicated asteroid searcher cannot stop cloud preventing observations, nor can he control the Moon which, when full, makes the sky so bright that it is impossible to search for faint objects. Nevertheless, given a little bit of luck, the asteroid could be discovered while still a considerable distance from Earth.

The true significance of the discovery would not be immediately apparent, since at first it would look like just another new Apollo object. Only after a few nights of further observations would it be possible to calculate the object's orbit, and only then would the possibility of a close approach to the Earth be appreciated. At this stage it is unlikely that there would be any real concern about the risk of an actual collision. Most interest would be concentrated on defining the orbit more accurately to allow detailed observations by large ground-based telescopes. News of the discovery would soon spread, encouraging other astronomers to search for the new object and to calculate its orbit. As more observations were made – and the probable error in the orbital calculations reduced – it would gradually become clear that a major disaster could be imminent. The astronomers involved would then be faced with the awful implications of their discovery.

A direct hit on the Earth is so improbable that is is almost certain that the astronomers concerned would want to make more measurements before announcing their results. These confirming observations would take at least another 24 hours, probably longer. Even under the most favourable circumstances, at least five days would have elapsed between the first sighting of the asteroid and the realization that it was on a collision course with the Earth.

Unfortunately, with the asteroid travelling at 20 kilometres a second, the gap between the asteroid and the Earth would be closing very quickly. Allowing for the fact that the asteroid would be following a curved path towards the point of impact, not travelling along the shortest straight line, it would be likely to strike the Earth within a month of being discovered. For comparison, comet IRAS-Araki-Alcock, which missed the Earth by an astronomically insignificant 5,000,000 kilometres in May 1983, was discovered only 16 days before its closest approach. A comet is much brighter than an asteroid, hence easier to discover, so it is clear that the warning of an asteroid impact could be very short indeed.

It seems unlikely that even under ideal circumstances there would be more than a few months' warning of the impending collision; quite possibly the time before impact could be measured in days. In the absence of an existing asteroid defence system, almost certainly nothing could be done to avert disaster. The only possible option would be to try to predict the precise point of impact and then attempt to reduce the loss of life by evacuating the threatened area. Since the impact of a 10–kilometre asteroid would produce a crater about 100 kilometres in diameter, and blast- and shockwaves would devastate areas thousands of kilometres from the crater, even this is barely practical. If the impact were to occur in one of the world's oceans – which is quite probable – the immediate threat would be to coastal areas which might be inundated by the resulting tidal waves. Under these circumstances the number of casualties might just be reduced by evacuation of the threatened coastlines, but this would be a mammoth undertaking, even for the industrialized nations.

Trying to minimize the immediate loss of life may be largely irrelevant if the ecological effects of a large asteroid impact are as severe as believed. In such circumstances it is difficult to imagine what steps could be taken to avoid total disaster. Factors quite beyond human control would determine whether or not mankind would survive.

It would be more probable that a new Apollo asteroid was discovered on an orbit which might result in a collision on a subsequent approach to Earth. For example, the preliminary orbit for a newly discovered asteroid might indicate that it would pass close to the Earth on its next-but-one orbit. A close approach would be of considerable scientific interest, and at the asteroid's next appearance – even if it was quite distant from the Earth – there would be a campaign of observations to refine the calculated orbit as much as possible. The initial objective would be to ensure the best possible scientific return from the forthcoming close approach, but the detailed observations might indicate that the asteroid was actually on a collision course, with an impact only one or two years ahead.

Although the rules of the International Astronomical Union stipulate that the orbit of a new asteroid must be known with considerable accuracy before it can be named, it might be acceptable to bend these rules a little and name such an important object immediately. Following the tradition of naming astronomical objects after figures from mythology, it may be appropriate to name this new asteroid Damocles, after the courtier of Dionysus who, having displeased his master, was seated at a banquet with a naked sword suspended above his head by a single thread.

Unfortunately – because of the inevitable uncertainties in calculating the orbit of an object which has been seen at only two appearances – there might well be considerable doubt about the conclusion that Damocles was on a collision course. In astronomical terms the Earth is a very small target, and even a tiny inaccuracy in the orbit calculated for the asteroid could mean the difference between a spectacularly near miss and an even more spectacular direct hit. The final result of these extra observations might be a prediction that the asteroid would probably strike the Earth, but that the precise point of impact was uncertain and a very near miss was still a possibility. The potentially dire consequences of such a prediction make it interesting to speculate whether any astronomer would be brave enough to announce his results publicly and risk inevitable ridicule if he turned out to be wrong. None the less, it is unlikely that the implications of such a discovery could be kept secret for long, since many different astronomers would be working on the orbit of the asteroid and all would eventually reach the same answer.

The possbility of a collision with Damocles could hardly be ignored. It is therefore quite likely that there would be a programme of further observations to remove any doubts about the danger to the Earth. This might require telescopes much larger than those usually used for asteroid research. Even the giant 200–inch telescope at Mount Palomar in California might be pressed into service. After several months of extra observations and improved orbital calculations there would be little doubt – at least in the minds of the astronomers involved – that the sword of Damocles was about to fall.

Assuming that the predicted impact was one to two years away – as it could well be if Damocles were in a typical Earth-crossing orbit – the world would be faced with an awesome decision. What, if anything, should be done? The simplest course would be to do nothing, and hope that the asteroid would miss the Earth completely. However, after several months of concentrated study, the size and destructive power of Damocles should have been well established, and if the Earth-colliding orbit was confirmed it is almost certain that simply hoping for the best would not be considered good enough. Mankind would be forced to act.

There are three options open to a world facing the catastrophe of a cosmic impact. The first is to attempt to divert the projectile so that it goes harmlessly past the Earth. The second is to break it into several pieces in the hope that most of the fragments miss the Earth, and accept the risk that the remainder might still do considerable damage. The third is to try and blast the entire asteroid to dust and small pieces which would burn up completely on entering the Earth's atmosphere.

The possibility of breaking Damocles into small pieces and gambling that none of the large fragments would fall on Earth can probably be rejected. It has almost all the difficulties of the alternatives, but few of the advantages of either. In particular there is still considerable risk that at least some fragments would fall on populated areas, and the total material damage caused by a rain of small objects might be considerable. The environmental effects of multiple impacts by kilometre-sized objects are also unknown and might be as serious as those of a single large object. For example, the total amount of dust injected into the atmosphere might be similar because the craters would be spread over a wide area, dispersing the dust more efficiently in the hours following the bombardment. Finally, even if calculations showed that there was little or no risk to the environment from a rain of small asteroid fragments, the political risk of one superpower accidentally diverting a large fragment into the territory of the other could not be ignored. It might be difficult to prove after the event that such a catastrophe was simply the result of bad fortune.

The remaining alternatives – reducing the asteroid to pieces too small to survive atmospheric entry (literally blowing it to dust) or attempting to alter its course away from the Earth – both have points in their favour. It is worth considering both in more detail.

Attempting to destroy the asteroid completely might seem the best solution, since this removes the threat from Damocles for ever. In fact this impression is not real – should Damocles be diverted successfully it is extremely unlikely that it could threaten the Earth again in the foreseeable future. It is almost inconceivable that a diversion of Damocles would merely postpone the collision for a few years.

The real merit of destruction over diversion is that it can – and probably must – be carried out at extremely short range. This has several important advantages. Firstly it allows the maximum time for preparation before mounting the attack on the asteroid, a vital consideration when the time available is so short. Secondly, an interception close to the Earth means that the missiles launched towards Damocles need operate in space for only a short period, reducing the likelihood of failures in the vital electrical or mechanical systems of the hastily prepared space vehicles. Finally the entire mission, including navigation and final guidance

171

towards the target, would occur close to the Earth. This would ease considerably problems of communicating with the missiles.

Unfortunately, there are also major drawbacks associated with a short-range interception. The main one is that there is no margin for error. If the strike failed to destroy Damocles, there would be no time for a second attempt. This point is especially telling since no one knows with any certainty how much explosive energy is required to pulverize a large asteroid, although it would obviously take nuclear weapons of considerable size. The political sensitivity of orbital nuclear weapon tests means that little is known about the behaviour of nuclear explosions in the vacuum of space; this compounds the difficulty of estimating the missiles' effectiveness.

These uncertainties – and the fact that we would not know the exact size and composition of Damocles until a short time before impact – mean that estimates of the total number of nuclear warheads needed for the attack would be little more than educated guesswork. Accordingly the plan would need to be highly conservative and allow a large safety margin, so that many missiles would be needed both to ensure success in the event of a failure of one or more launches, and to carry the requisite number of warheads to the target.

The need to use many separate missiles introduces major problems of its own. To produce the maximum destructive effect, all the missiles would have to attack Damocles together. Failure to achieve this concerted attack would risk splitting Damocles into large fragments, each of which would then have to be destroyed separately. At close range, and with little time to determine the fragment's trajectories, this extra task of sweeping up the pieces would be extremely difficult, if not impossible.

The difficulties of mounting a concerted attack on Damocles would go far beyond the problems of controlling simultaneously a large number of separate missiles. Unless the warheads were to detonate together, it is highly likely that the explosion of the first weapon would destroy or disable some or all of the remainder, preventing the destruction of the asteroid. The mutual destruction of incoming warheads is caused by the intense pulse of electro-magnetic energy produced in a nuclear explosion. Large numbers

172

of gamma rays and X-rays are emitted and – travelling at the speed of light – these might penetrate the sensitive electronics of subsequent missiles, rendering them uncontrollable. The major powers are developing special techniques to protect military systems against being crippled in this way during a nuclear war, but the details of this work remain a closely guarded secret.

The uncertainties associated with the near-simultaneous detonation of many separate nuclear warheads, and the impossibility of carrying out any truly realistic tests before the attack on Damocles, mean that the risks of a last-minute attempt to destroy the asteroid would probably be considered too great. The only remaining option would be to attempt the first feat of astro-engineering, and divert Damocles into an orbit which would carry it harmlessly clear of the Earth. For the first time in mankind's history, the technology to attempt such a diversion is within our grasp; although it would push the world's resources to the very limit.

To appreciate what is involved in diverting an asteroid, we must consider some of the principles behind celestial mechanics, the rules governing the motion of objects in space. Since the time of Isaac Newton it has been known that all the members of the solar system travel in curved paths under the influence of gravitational forces, notably that of the Sun. Newton also showed that to cause an object to change its path through space, a force must be applied to it; the effect of such a force depends on the mass of the object. The more massive the object, the larger the force required to change its path.

The mass of an Apollo asteroid, although astronomically insignificant, is very large by terrestrial standards. An asteroid 10 kilometres in diameter with a density like that of the Moon (about 3 grams per cubic centimetre) has a mass of about one and a half million million tonnes. To change the velocity of such an object by just one metre per second demands a force of fifteen hundred million million Newtons. This is equivalent to firing the main engines of a Saturn 5 moonrocket continuously for about 13 years. Normal space propulsion systems are quite inadequate to deflect Damocles. Even if it were possible to transport large rocket engines (and their fuel) to the asteroid and set them up on its surface, there would not be enough time for them to have much effect on the object's trajectory.

The only technique which might have any chance of diverting Damocles in time requires nuclear weapons, but in a quite different way from the destructive attack discussed earlier. This alternative approach relies on the fact that when there is an explosion near the ground a large quantity of target material is ejected from the site of the explosion. On Earth most of this material falls back to the ground, forming an ejecta blanket around the crater, but on an asteroid the very weak gravitational field means that most of the ejected material would be hurled straight into space. In effect, the material blasted off the asteroid would act like the exhaust gases of a rocket motor, producing an equal and opposite reaction on the asteroid. This is similar to a brief firing of a thruster on a spacecraft, and would cause a small change in the asteroid's trajectory. To calculate the effect of a single nuclear explosion on the course of a 10–kilometre asteroid, we need to know the mass and velocity of the material ejected during the explosion. From this information we can calculate the force produced, and hence the change in velocity of the asteroid. These values all depend on the explosive power of the weapon used, and on the nature of the target material.

The largest nuclear warhead used by the United States missile forces has a destructive power of 18 megatons and is fitted to the Titan II missiles which form part of the American nuclear deterrent. These would be too small for the attack on Damocles; we would need to assemble more powerful weapons. A warhead with a destructive power of about 100 megatons would probably be more realistic. Using studies of the effects of both nuclear and conventional explosives on the Earth, we can predict that a 100-megaton explosion on, or near, the surface of a rocky asteroid would produce a crater about 500 metres in diameter. This would eject about 700,000,000 tonnes of material with an average velocity of about 3 to 4 kilometres per second. One estimate of the effect of this tremendous explosion is that it would change the velocity of Damocles by about one-fiftieth of a metre per second.

If different assumptions are made about the way the total

energy of the bomb is converted into an acceleration of the asteroid, a velocity change 10 or 20 times as great may be possible, but even with this more optimistic value the effect of a single explosion on the path of the asteroid would be very small. We would obviously have to use more than one warhead to achieve a significant deflection. An attempt to achieve multiple nuclear strikes on an Earth-approaching asteroid would, however, be a major undertaking, almost certainly requiring considerable international co-operation.

The magnitude and complexity of the task – expecially in view of the very small changes to the asteroid's course which could conceivably be achieved – might suggest that a deflection mission is beyond the capability of twentieth-century technology. In certain circumstances this may well be so, but in others even a small change in the asteroid's velocity might be sufficient to save the Earth from disaster. The precise details depend very critically on the orbit of Earth and asteroid, and on the timing of the deflection attempt. If the asteroid is attacked while still a long way from Earth, the deflection could be smaller than if the attempt is made at close range, but a long-range attack on Damocles would take more powerful rockets to launch the missiles and more complex spacecraft to carry the weapons to their target. This increases the technical difficulties of the mission, so one of the first tasks in planning an asteroid deflection would be a detailed study to determine the best possible time to carry out the interception.

If this study showed that a deflection attempt was feasible, how might it be accomplished? Imagine we discovered that a strike by a series of 100-megaton bombs would alter the course of Damocles enough to steer it away from the Earth. This was the basis of a short theoretical study in 1967 on the possibility of diverting the Apollo asteroid Icarus, so it is a reasonable starting point. The imaginary asteroid Damocles is larger than Icarus, but the techniques needed to divert it are similar and do not depend on the size of the target. The effect of such a strike on a 10-kilometre asteroid would be small, but might be enough.

A multiple nuclear strike on a rapidly appoaching asteroid would be an extremely complex task requiring the co-ordination of many diverse activities. Suitable missiles would have to be designed, manufactured and tested in a very short time. Simultaneously, we would need numerous computer simulations of attack strategies so that a series of alternative plans could be available in the event of last-minute delays or failures. Then, in quick succession, the missiles should be launched on to courses that would bring them to the target asteroid at intervals of a few days. We would have to control this nuclear armada over a distance of millions of kilometres, and to observe the effects of the nuclear strikes on the asteroid. Fortunately the technical and managerial resources to make such a strike are probably already available; they have been developed over a quarter of a century of spaceflight. All we would need is the political will to commit such immense resources and to bring together the necessary expertise from the scientific, technical and military communities.

Consider first the nuclear warheads required for the attacks. We have now spent more than four decades developing nuclear weapons of enormous destructive potential. Early ballistic missiles were comparatively inaccurate, so the warheads developed for them were extremely powerful. The destructive power of these weapons was so enormous that errors in the aiming of the missile were unimportant, and they were known colloquially as 'city busters'. As the missiles' accuracy improved, and it became possible to install multiple warheads in each, the size of the warheads was reduced. Today's American Minuteman 3 missile carries three 200-kiloton warheads. These are almost a hundred times less powerful than those of the less accurate Titan II missiles developed a decade earlier. None the less, the production of a limited number of 100-megaton warheads should present no major technical problems. A crash programme to develop new and very large nuclear warheads is more likely to raise obstacles of a political nature, especially once it was learned that the weapons were designed to be placed in space. To avoid such difficulties we would need to ensure that the project was internationally monitored.

It might seem desirable for all the major nations to co-operate on the production of the missiles, but in practice the project would be so complex that there would probably not be time to bring together designers and engineers from many different nations. A more sensible plan would be to split the project into different, more or less independent, tasks – astronomical studies of Damocles, planning attack strategies, developing the missiles – and then divide these up between small groups of nations. An international management team should be set up to co-ordinate these activities, but the individual tasks could be accomplished by existing organizations such as NASA and the International Astronomical Union.

As well as the warheads for the attack on Damocles, we would need a method of launching them towards their target. Existing missiles would be unsuitable, since they are designed to carry their deadly cargoes on short flights between two points on the Earth's surface, and are not powerful enough to reach orbit. Assuming that the attack on Damocles is to be led by the United States, the space shuttle would probably be used to lift the individual missiles into parking orbits around the Earth. After a comprehensive checkout by astronauts and ground control, each missile would be placed on course towards Damocles by one of the rocket stages routinely used to boost satellites into orbits beyond the reach of the shuttle. The best upper stage would probably be the Centaur rocket which, in combination with the shuttle, launches large interplanetary spaceprobes. Centaur can launch a fairly heavy spacecraft to Jupiter and should certainly be adequate to launch large payloads towards Damocles. The space shuttle is also the only system able to launch several large payloads in quick succession. Even if suitable conventional rockets were available, it is unlikely that enough missiles could be launched during the time available.

To achieve the maximum deflection of Damocles, the attack would have to take place at a great distance from the Earth, so the missiles would need to be able to make small course corrections during their flight towards the asteroid. Rather than encumber the warhead design with the complex systems needed to navigate through space, the nuclear weapons would be carried on a separate, custom-built spacecraft, probably a modified version of an existing interplanetary probe. Using a proven design for the carrier would reduce the risk of technical failure, since the spacecraft itself would already be fully developed and tested. This vehicle would carry all the equipment necessary to protect the warhead during its cruise towards Damocles, and to make the necessary course corrections. The carrier would also be equipped with cameras, and probably a radar system, to help aim the warhead at its target during the final stages of the attack. Interestingly, a few years ago NASA did propose the use of a very simple interplanetary craft whose sole purpose would be to carry an atmospheric probe to the planet Jupiter, then aim the probe at the planet and release it. Although this idea was later abandoned, it does provide the basis for the design of a vehicle to carry a nuclear warhead to Damocles.

The idea of using a separate carrier spacecraft also provides an opportunity to monitor the effects of the nuclear strike. Once the bomb has been released towards its target the carrier can be manoeuvred as far as possible from Damocles in order to observe the subsequent explosion. The purpose of such observations would be to determine the effect of the attack and enable us to modify the subsequent strikes to achieve the maximum effect. If the carrier survived the explosion, we could also use photographs taken from the spacecraft to estimate the change to the asteroid's orbit. A secondary objective of the carrier mission would be to gather scientific data about the asteroid for comparison with ground-based observations, improving our overall understanding of the Apollo objects.

The nuclear warhead itself would have to be designed to the highest possible standards to ensure the safety of ground personnel and the shuttle astronauts during launch, and to maximize the chances of a successful mission. We would also have to package the weapon in such a way that, in the event of the shuttle being destroyed during launch, there is no risk of a premature explosion or of fallout contaminating the area around the launch site. This would necessitate a protective casing around the warhead during launch and a suitable safe-arm system to prevent accidental detonation. The launch protection shroud can of course be retained in the shuttle after the missile is deployed, then returned to Earth for use on a subsequent launch. The missile would be armed before being boosted out of parking orbit. If it failed to arm itself when instructed, it would be retrieved and returned to Earth for repairs. As a final safety measure, a self-destruct device would be fitted to render the weapon harmless if it were to be accidentally placed into the wrong orbit.

Once safely on its way to Damocles, each warhead would be virtually inert, carrying out only occasional test procedures during the cruise towards the target. Shortly before release from the carrier vehicle the warhead would be fully activated and given a final check. One of the most critical items in this final check would be the fuse which would actually detonate the bomb. To achieve the maximum effect – that is, to blast out as large a crater as possible and produce the largest impulse on the asteroid – the warhead must explode as close to the surface as possible. However, if a warhead were to collide with Damocles before being detonated it would be destroyed before it could explode. To ensure that the warhead detonates at the correct distance from the surface of Damocles, a short-range radar fuse would be fitted and set to detonate the bomb at a height of a few hundred metres. As a backup – to allow for the possibility that the weapon might miss Damocles completely – the fuse might also be set to detonate should the range to the asteroid fall to a minimum value and then start to increase again.

Following the explosion, we could use observations from the carrier vehicle and ground-based telescopes to recompute the asteroid's orbit, and to assess if there was still a risk to the Earth. If we found that a collision had not been averted, then a second strike would be made using one of the vehicles en route to Damocles. Eventually, after several strikes, the deflection manoeuvre would be complete and any remaining missiles would be deactivated or commanded to self-destruct.

A few months later Damocles would fly past the Earth and doubtless be of considerable interest to both professional and amateur astronomers. Despite its close approach, it would probably not be obvious to the naked eye and the asteroid itself might well escape the attention of most of the world's population. Even so Damocles might produce one final reminder of its passage, because much of the material blasted off the asteroid during the repeated nuclear attacks would still be orbiting close to the original Earth-intercepting orbit. When our planet passed through this stream of debris there would be a brief but spectacular meteor shower, and perhaps a number of meteorite falls. These small stones would be the only fragments of Damocles ever to reach the surface of the Earth.

The idea that asteroids might collide with the Earth is fairly new. Historically, there has been much more concern about the threat from comets. The ratio between comet and asteroid impacts was discussed in Chapter 3; it is generally believed that no more than a quarter to a tenth of large terrestrial craters were produced by comets, so this danger is even less than the threat from Apollo asteroids. This is fortunate, since diverting a comet might be much more difficult than attacking an Apollo asteroid.

The difficulties arise because comets are active and brighten as they approach the Sun. Although the brightening – caused by the evaporation of ice from the surface of the nucleus – makes them much easier to detect, the rocket effect of material boiling off the comet produces 'non-gravitational forces' which move the body away from its predicted path. This makes it extremely difficult to predict accurately the future position of a comet. There would be little or no chance of reliably predicting a cometary impact far enough ahead to plan a deflection mission.

In practice, even if time permitted, a deflection attempt on a comet would almost certainly be impossible since the attacking missiles would probably be destroyed by high-speed collisions with dust grains in the coma long before they could reach the central nucleus and detonate. Even if the warheads could be protected against dust, and somehow steered towards the invisible nucleus, the effects of the resulting explosions would be highly unpredictable. This is because a cometary nucleus is both small and fragile. Strikes by nuclear weapons would probably fragment the nucleus and dramatically increase the comet's activity as fresh ice from the interior was exposed. This burst of activity would almost certainly increase the density of dust in the coma, threatening the following missiles with destruction and producing new non-gravitational forces which would make the calculation of the comet's future path even more difficult.

Fortunately comet nuclei are quite small – typically only a few kilometres across – so the global effects of a comet impact may be less severe than a collision with a large Apollo asteroid, although there would be disastrous local ones. A threat to the Earth from one of the few very large comets believed to exist is extremely unlikely and can safely be ignored.

The diversion of an Apollo asteroid – or an attack on a comet if one were feasible – would be close to the limit of current technology, but these limits will soon be left behind as mankind moves into the next century. Within a decade there will be a permanently-manned space station in orbit around the Earth, and from this will develop a space transportation system which will allow humanity the freedom of near-Earth space. As civilization expands into the solar system, exploring and exploiting what Professor Gerard O'Neill called 'The High Frontier', the demand for resources to build large structures in orbit will increase far beyond the capability of routine space shuttle flights to satisfy them. O'Neill envisages building huge orbiting power satellites using materials mined from the Moon and processed in self-sustaining orbiting cities, each home for thousands of people. The Apollo asteroids may be a possible source of raw materials for these advanced space colonies.

The advantage of mining the Apollo asteroids is that some are believed to contain elements which cannot easily be extracted from lunar material. Moonrock returned to Earth during the 1960s and 1970s is almost totally devoid of water, carbon and nitrogen, yet all these would be needed in vast quantities by the colonists on the high frontier. Carbonaceous asteroids contain considerable quantities of these elements, and other classes of Apollo objects are richer than lunar soil in metallic iron and nickel. In the very long term, asteroid mining might be the most economic way to supply space colonies.

To exploit the resources of the asteroids we would need a capability far greater than is necessary to change the velocity of an Apollo object by a few metres per second with nuclear weapons. Asteroid mining demands a major alteration in an asteroid's orbit, allowing relocation around the Earth or Moon, or at one of the gravitationally stable positions in the Earth-Moon system known

181

as the Lagrangian points. This involves changing the object's velocity by several kilometres per second, in a precisely controlled manner. No normal means of rocket propulsion could possible do this in a reasonable time, and even a major bombardment by large nuclear weapons would hardly be practical, since the asteroid material would be of no value if it was contaminated by radioactive debris from the nuclear bombs. The relocation of an asteroid is a visionary project which requires bold new concepts in space operations – techniques beyond our present capability, but within the grasp of a society familiar with routine operations in space and on the surface of the Moon.

The key to large-scale astro-engineering may lie with a device known as an electromagnetic mass driver. The mass driver is a sort of magnetic catapult which uses a linear induction motor to accelerate a trolley along a long straight track. A magnetic levitation system is used to lift the trolley just clear of the track, virtually eliminating any friction between them. Similar magnetically levitated vehicles are already being developed for use on Earth.

The mass driver was originally conceived as a means of launching huge quantities of material from the Moon to one of O'Neill's space cities. On an airless world like the Moon, with an abundant supply of solar energy to provide electricity, a bucket of material can be accelerated to escape velocity while still attached to the mass driver trolley. By releasing the bucket at the correct moment, bucket and contents can be aimed at a colony thousands of kilometres away in space, while the launching trolley can be slowed down and returned to its starting point to launch another load of material. By suitably compressing the lunar soil it may even be possible to dispense with the bucket and launch a huge pellet of material directly into space. Although this use of a mass driver is unusual in concept there are no theoretical objections, although the engineering challenge is certainly great. Small working models of mass drivers have already been built and have achieved accelerations greater than 30 times the force of gravity.

In principle, a mass driver could be operated on any world with low gravity and no atmosphere. Since mass drivers need prodigious amounts of electrical power, they are best suited to the inner solar system where solar cells can be used to tap the Sun's energy. Apollo asteroids are obvious candidates for a mass-driver installation and, unlike the lunar example, the asteroidal mass driver can be used as a propulsion system. The stream of material fired off the asteroid acts like a rocket engine, accelerating the asteroid in the opposite direction. Compared with the atomic weapons proposed to divert Damocles, which ejected large amounts of material almost instantaneously, the asteroidal mass driver ejects much smaller quantities continuously over a period of many years. This provides a more controllable thrust, allowing precision navigation of the asteroid. This small, but steady, thrust can be supplemented by using close approaches to one or more of the inner planets to modify the asteroid's trajectory, like the gravity-assist manoeuvres used by interplanetary space probes.

Before such a major and expensive undertaking could be considered, we would have to ensure that the asteroid selected for diversion would contain an economic quantity of the desired raw materials. This we could achieve by extensive astronomical studies of a range of candidates, followed by spaceprobe rendezvous missions to make on-the-spot measurements of the selected asteroid's composition. Next, we would undertake detailed mathematical studies to determine the most efficient trajectory to move the asteroid from its existing orbit to its new location. Only once every stage of the operation had been worked out in great detail would the first miners set out to rendezvous with the chosen asteroid.

On arriving at the asteroid and manoeuvring their spacecraft to fly in formation with it, the astronauts would descend to the surface using jet packs derived from those now used regularly by space-shuttle astronauts. One of their first actions might well be to string a cat's cradle of safety lines across the surface to provide handholds and reduce the risk of accidentally drifting off the asteroid, whose gravity would be so weak as to be almost unnoticeable. Using maps based on photographs provided by unmanned pathfinder probes, the astronauts would set up the mass driver and its solar panels according to a carefully arranged plan.

Once the mass driver was ready, the first step would be to use it to stop the asteroid's natural rotation so that the final thrust could be applied in the correct direction. Then the mass driver would be repositioned to begin the long process of actually moving the asteroid to its new location, which might take several decades. During the long cruise the mass driver would work automatically under computer control, with only occasional visits by astronauts to carry out routine maintenance and running repairs. Once the asteroid was safely relocated, the main group of miners would arrive and begin to remove the materials needed by the orbiting factories.

Although the idea of rearranging the solar system in this way may seem absurd, it is important to remember that an Apollo object only 200 metres in diameter contains about 10,000,000 tonnes of material, much of which may be suitable for large-scale orbital manufacture. It would be extremely difficult to lift such large quantities into space from the Earth's surface. If the huge space settlements envisaged by O'Neill ever become a reality, then the exploitation of the asteroids is probably inevitable. The technological challenge of asteroid mining may appear insuperable today, but to a spacefaring society a hundred or more years in the future it may present a task no greater than that faced by the United States when, just days after America's first 15-minute spaceflight, it committed itself to landing a man on the Moon within a decade.

Epilogue

Any reader concerned about the personal threat from a cosmic impact may be reassured to know that during the writing of this book I have found only one reliable example of personal injury as the result of a meteorite fall. On 30 November 1954 Mrs E.H. Hodges of Sylacauga, Alabama, was resting on her sofa after lunch. A meteorite weighing about 2 kilograms crashed through her roof, bounced off a radio set and struck her on the thigh. Mrs Hodges received some bruises.

John Davies
February 1986

Appendix 1

A List of Asteroids in Earth-crossing Orbits

Number & name		Discovered	Perihelion AU	Aphelion AU	Eccentricity	Inclination°	Period years
3200	Phaethon	1983	0.14	2.47	0.894	22.8	1.48
1566	Icarus	1949	0.19	1.97	0.827	23.0	1.12
2212	Hephaistos	1978	0.36	3.97	0.835	11.9	3.17
1974MA		1974	0.42	3.13	0.762	37.8	2.37
2101	Adonis	1936	0.44	3.30	0.764	1.4	2.56
2340	Hathor	1976	0.46	1.22	0.450	5.9	0.77
2100	Ra-Shalom	1978	0.47	1.20	0.437	15.8	0.75
1954XA		1954	0.51	1.05	0.345	3.9	0.69
1982TA		1982	0.53	4.07	0.769	12.1	3.48
1984QA		1984	0.53	1.45	0.468	9.9	0.98
1985KB		1985	0.53	3.88	0.760	4.6	3.28
1864	Daedelus	1971	0.56	2.36	0.615	22.1	1.76
1865	Cerberus	1971	0.58	1.58	0.467	16.1	1.12
—	Hermes	1937	0.62	2.66	0.624	6.2	2.11
1981	Midas	1973	0.62	2.93	0.650	39.8	2.37
2201	Oljato	1947	0.63	3.72	0.712	2.5	3.20
1981VA		1981	0.63	4.22	0.744	22.0	3.78
1862	Apollo	1932	0.65	2.29	0.560	6.4	1.78
1979XB		1979	0.65	3.88	0.713	24.9	3.40
2063	Bacchus	1977	0.70	1.45	0.349	9.4	1.12
1685	Toro	1948	0.77	1.96	0.436	9.4	1.60
1983LC		1983	0.77	4.50	0.711	1.5	4.27
2062	Aten	1976	0.79	1.14	0.182	18.9	0.96
2135	Aristaeus	1977	0.79	2.40	0.503	23.0	2.02
1983VA		1983	0.81	3.67	0.638	15.4	3.35
1982HR		1982	0.82	1.60	0.322	2.7	1.33
6743 P-L		1960	0.82	2.42	0.493	7.3	2.06
1983TF2		1983	0.82	3.62	0.387	7.8	4.22
2329	Orthos	1976	0.82	3.99	0.658	24.4	3.72
1620	Geographos	1951	0.83	1.66	0.335	13.3	1.38
1959LM		1959	0.83	1.85	0.379	3.3	1.55
1950DA		1950	0.84	2.53	0.502	12.1	2.18
1866	Sisyphus	1972	0.87	2.92	0.540	41.1	2.38

Number & name		Discovered	Perihelion AU	Aphelion AU	Eccentricity	Inclination°	Period years
1978CA		1978	0.88	1.37	0.215	26.1	1.19
1973NA		1973	0.88	4.04	0.642	68.1	3.86
1863	Antinous	1948	0.89	3.63	0.606	18.4	3.40
2102	Tantalus	1975	0.91	1.67	0.298	64.0	1.97
1982BB		1982	0.91	1.91	0.355	20.9	1.67
6344 P-L		1960	0.94	4.21	0.635	4.6	4.14
1982DB		1982	0.95	2.02	0.360	1.2	1.81
1979VA		1979	0.98	4.29	0.627	2.8	4.29
1985PA		1985	1.00	1.86	0.301	56.3	1.71
1982XB		1982	1.01	2.70	0.454	3.9	2.54
1985KD		1985	1.01	3.40	0.542	13.7	3.26
1981ET3		1981	1.02	2.52	0.422	22.2	2.35
2608	Seneca	1978	1.02	3.93	0.587	15.6	3.91
1980PA		1980	1.04	2.82	0.459	2.2	2.68
1980AA		1980	1.05	2.73	0.444	4.2	2.60
2061	Anza	1960	1.05	3.48	0.537	3.7	3.40
1915	Quetzalcoatl	1953	1.05	3.99	0.583	20.5	4.00
1943	Anteros	1973	1.06	1.80	0.256	8.7	1.71
1917	Cuyo	1968	1.06	3.23	0.505	24.0	3.15
1983RD		1983	1.07	3.12	0.488	9.5	3.04
1221	Amor	1932	1.08	2.76	0.436	11.9	2.66
1980WF		1980	1.08	3.38	0.514	6.4	3.33
1981QB		1981	1.08	3.39	0.518	37.1	3.35
1983RB		1983	1.09	3.35	0.490	18.0	3.30
1982DV		1982	1.10	2.96	0.457	5.9	2.89
1985JA		1985	1.10	2.03	0.296	35.1	1.96
1982YA		1982	1.11	5.09	0.641	33.2	5.46
1627	Ivar	1929	1.12	2.60	0.397	8.4	2.54
1580	Betulia	1950	1.12	3.27	0.490	52.0	3.25
2202	Pele	1972	1.12	3.46	0.510	8.8	3.47
433	Eros	1898	1.13	1.78	0.223	10.6	1.76
887	Alinda	1918	1.15	3.88	0.544	9.1	2.54

N.B. 433 Eros and 887 Alinda are included because although they do not cross the Earth's orbit at present, they can evolve into Earth-crossing orbits under the gravitational influence of the other planets.

Appendix 2

Impact Structures on the Earth's Surface

Notes	Crater name	Latitude	Longitude	Diameter (km)	Age (my)
	Amguid, Algeria	25 05 N	4 23 E	0.45	< 0.1
	Aouelloul, Mauritania	20 15 N	12 41 W	0.37	3.1
	Araguainha Dome, Brazil	16 46 S	52 59 W	40 °	<250
	Bee Bluff (Uvalde), USA	29 02 N	99 51 W	2.4	< 40
	Beyenchime-Salaatin, USSR	71 50 N	123 30 E	8	< 65
	Boltysh, USSR	48 45 N	32 10 E	25	100
Source of Ivory Coast tektites	Bosumtwi, Ghana	6 32 N	1 25 W	10.5	1.3
	'BP' Structure, Libya	25 19 N	24 20 E	2.8°	<120
	Brent, Canada	46 05 N	78 29 W	3.8	450
	Carswell, Canada	58 27 N	109 30 W	37 °	485
	Charlevoix, Canada	47 32 N	70 18 W	46 °	360
Double impact see Chapter 4	Clearwater L. East, Canada	56 05 N	74 07 W	22	290
	Clearwater L. West, Canada	56 13 N	74 30 W	32 °	290
	Crooked Creek, USA	37 50 N	91 23 W	5.6°	320*
	Decaturville, USA	37 54 N	92 43 W	6 °	<300
	Deep Bay, Canada	56 24 N	102 59 W	12	100*
	Dellen, Sweden	61 55 N	16 32 E	15 °	230
	El'gygytgyn, USSR	67 30 N	172 05 E	19	3.5
See Chapter 5	Flynn Creek, USA	36 16 N	85 37 W	3.8	360
	Goat Paddock, Australia	18 20 S	126 40 E	5	50
Comet impact?	Gosse's Bluff, Australia	23 50 S	132 19 E	22	130
	Gow Lake, Canada	56 27 N	104 29 W	5 °	<200
	Haughton, Canada	75 22 N	89 40 W	20	< 15
	Holleford, Canada	44 28 N	76 38 W	2	550*
	Ile Rouleau, Canada	50 41 N	73 53 W	4 °	<300
	Ilintsy, USSR	48 45 N	28 00 E	4.5°	495
	Janisjarvi, USSR	61 58 N	30 55 E	14 °	700
	Kaluga, USSR	54 30 N	36 15 E	15	360
	Kamensk, USSR	48 20 N	40 15 E	25 °	65
	Kara, USSR	69 10 N	65 00 E	50 °	57
	Karla, USSR	57 54 N	48 00 E	10	10
	Kelly West, Australia	19 30 S	132 50 E	2.5°	<550

Crater name	Latitude	Longitude	Diameter (km)	Age (my)	Notes
Kentland, USA	40 45 N	87 24 W	13 °	300	
Kjardla, USSR	57 00 N	22 42 E	4	500	
Kursk, USSR	51 40 N	36 00 E	5 °	250*	
Lac Couture, Canada	60 08 N	75 18 W	8 °	420	
Lac La Moinerie, Canada	57 26 N	66 36 W	8 °	400	
Lappajarvi, Finland	63 09 N	23 42 E	14 °	77*	
Liverpool, Australia	12 24 S	134 03 E	1.6	150*	
Logoisk, USSR	54 12 N	27 48 E	17	100	
Lonar, India	19 58 N	76 31 E	1.8	0.05	
Manicouagan L., Canada	51 23 N	68 42 W	70 °	210	See Chapter 4
Manson, USA	42 35 N	94 31 W	32	< 70	
Mien Lake, Sweden	56 25 N	14 52 E	5 °	118	
Middlesboro, USA	36 37 N	83 44 W	6 °	300	
Misarai, USSR	54 00 N	23 54 E	5	500*	
Mishina Gora, USSR	58 40 N	28 00 E	9 °	<360	
Mistastin, Canada	55 53 N	63 18 W	28 °	38	
Monturaqui, Chile	23 56 S	68 17 W	0.46	1	Evidence of iron meteorites found
New Quebec, Canada	61 17 N	73 40 W	3.2	5	
Nicholson L., Canada	62 40 N	102 41 W	12.5°	<450	
'Oasis', Libya	24 35 N	24 24 E	11.5°	<120	
Obolon, USSR	49 30 N	32 55 E	15 °	160	
Ouarkziz, Algeria	29 00 N	7 33 W	3.5	< 70	
Patom, USSR	59 00 N	116 25 E	0.09	0.0003	
Pilot Lake, Canada	60 17 N	111 01 W	6 °	<300	
Popigai, USSR	71 30 N	111 00 E	100	39	
Puchezh-Katunki, USSR	57 06 N	43 35 E	80	183	
Redwing Creek, USA	47 40 N	102 30 W	9	200	
Riacháo Ring, Brazil	7 43 S	46 39 W	4	?	
Ries, Germany	48 53 N	10 37 E	24	14.8	Source of moldavites (tektites)
Rochechouart, France	45 49 N	00 05 E	23 °	160	
Rotmistrovka, USSR	49 00 N	32 00 E	5	70	
Saaksjarvi, Finland	61 23 N	22 25 E	5 °	490	
St Martin, Canada	51 47 N	98 33 W	23	225	
Serpent Mound, USA	39 02 N	83 24 W	6.4°	300	
Serra da Canghala, Brazil	8 05 S	46 52 W	12 °	<300	
Shunak, USSR	42 42 S	72 42 E	2.5	12	
Sierra Maderia, USA	30 36 N	102 55 W	13 °	100	
Siljan, Sweden	61 02 N	14 52 E	52 °	365	
Slate island, Canada	48 40 N	87 00 W	30 °	350	

Notes	Crater name	Latitude	Longitude	Diameter (km)	Age (my)
	Sobolev, USSR	46 18 N	138 52 E	0.05	0.002
	Soderfjarden, Finland	63 02 N	21 35 E	5.5°	600
	Spider, Australia	16 30 S	126 00 E	5 °	?
	Steen River, Canada	59 31 N	117 38 W	25	95
	Steinheim, Germany	48 41 N	10 04 E	3.4	14.8
	Strangways, Australia	15 12 S	133 35 E	24 °	< 600
	Sudbury, Canada	46 36 N	81 11 W	140 °	1840
	Tabun-Khara-Obo, Mongolia	44 06 N	109 36 E	1.3	< 30
	Talemzane, Algeria	33 19 N	04 02 E	1.75	< 3
	Teague, Australia	25 50 S	120 55 E	28 °	<1685
	Tenoumer, Mauritania	22 55 N	10 24 W	1.9	2.5
	Tin Bider, Algeria	27 36 N	5 07 E	6 °	< 70
	Vepriaj, USSR	55 06 N	24 36 E	8	160
	Vredefort, South Africa	27 00 S	27 30 E	140 °	1970
	Wanapitei L., Canada	46 44 N	80 44 W	8.5°	37
	Wells Creek, USA	36 23 N	87 40 W	14 °	200*
	West Hawk Lake, Canada	49 46 N	95 11 W	2.7	100*
	Zeleny Gai, USSR	48 07 N	32 09 E	1.4	120
	Zhamanshin, USSR	49 00 N	61 00 E	10	4.5

* indicates that the crater age is very uncertain
° indicates that the structure is very eroded
< less than
my million years

For more details see:
Grieve, R., Geological Society of America Special Paper 180, 25 (1982)
Grieve, R. and Robertson, P., ICARUS 38, 212–29 (1979)
Shoemaker, E., *Annual Reviews of Earth and Planet Science* 11, 461–94 (1983)

Bibliography

Readers wishing to investigate the subject of cosmic impacts in more detail should find that the following books and technical papers provide a useful starting point.

General Reading
Clube, V. and Napier, B., *The Cosmic Serpent* (Faber and Faber, London, 1982)
Greely, R., *Planetary Landscape* (Allen & Unwin, London, 1985)
Kelly Beatty, J., O'Leary, B., and Chaiken, A., *The New Solar System* (Cambridge University Press, Cambridge, 1981)
Krinov, E.L., *Giant Meteorites* (Pergamon Press, Oxford, 1966)
Sears, D.W., *The Nature and Origin of Meteorites* (Adam Hilger, Bristol, 1981)

Technical Papers
Alvarez, W.L., Alvarez, W., Asaro, F., and Michel, H. V., 'Extraterrestrial Cause for the Cretaceous-Tertiary Extinction', *Science* 208, 1095 (1980)
Davies, J.K., 'Is 3200 Phaethon a Dead Comet?', *Sky and Telescope*, October 1985
Hoffman, A., 'Patterns of family extinction depend on definition and geological timescale', *Nature* 315, 659 (1985)
McCall, G.J.H. (ed.), 'Meteorite Craters' (Benchmark Papers in Geology 36, Dowden, Hutchinson and Ross, Pennsylvania 1977)
O'Leary, B., 'Mining the Apollo-Amor Asteroids', *Science* 197, 363 (1977)
Officer, B.C., and Drake, L.C., 'Terminal Cretaceous Environmental Effects', *Science* 227, 1161 (1985)
Roddy, D.J., Pepin, R.O., and Merril, R.B., *Impact and Explosion Cratering* (Pergamon Press, New York, 1977)
Russell, D.A., 'The Enigma of the Extinction of the Dinosaurs',

Annual Reviews of Earth and Planet Sciences 7, 163 (1979)

Sekinina, Z., 'The Tunguska Event: No Cometary Signature in Evidence', *Astronomical Journal* 88, 1382 (1983)

Shoemaker, E.M., 'Large Body Impacts Through Geological Time', in *Patterns of Change in Earth Evolution* (eds Holland, H. D., Trendall, A. E., Springer-Verlag, Berlin, 1984)

Silver, L.T., Schultz, P.H. (eds), 'Geological Implications of Impacts of Large Asteroids and Comets on the Earth', Geological Society of America Special Paper 190 (1982)

Various authors writing on the fall of the Barwell Meteorite, *Journal of the British Astronomical Association* 76 (1965)

Index